International
Bottle Collectors'
Guide

International Bottle Collectors' Guide

by
Edward Fletcher

BLANDFORD PRESS
POOLE   DORSET

Blandford Press Ltd
Link House, West Street,
Poole, Dorset, BH15 1LL

First published 1975

© 1975 Edward Fletcher

ISBN 0 7137 0758 5

Text set in 12 on 13 Bembo and
printed in Great Britain by
Unwin Brothers Limited
The Gresham Press
Old Woking, Surrey
A member of Staples Printing Group

List of Contents

Introduction   9

1 The British Scene   13

Mineral waters—Codd-Hamilton hybrids—Inks—Bitters—
Sealed bottles—Case gins and Schnapps—Black glass—Acid
etched glass—Blue glass—Patent medicines—Stoneware—Baby
feeders—Sauces, pickles, and fruit jars—Miniatures—Pot lids—
Clay tobacco pipes—Modern bottles and reproductions—
Restored and repaired bottles—Glass sickness, iridescence, and
opalescence—Pontil marks

2 The Australian Scene   61

Mineral water patents—Inks—Bitters—Sealed bottles—Case gins
and Schnapps—Black glass—Acid etched glass—Blue glass—
Patent medicines—Stoneware—Baby feeders—Sauces, pickles
and fruit jars—Pot lids—Clay tobacco pipes—Modern bottles
and reproductions—Restored and repaired bottles—Glass
sickness, iridescence, and opalescence—Sun-coloured glass—
Pontil marks

3 The American Scene   95

Colonial bottles and Historical flasks—Bitters—Inks—Patent
medicines—Whiskies and gins—Mineral and Soda waters—Fruit
jars and household bottles—Stoneware—Baby feeders—Poison
bottles—Fire grenades—Reproduction bottles—Modern bottles—
Restored and repaired bottles—Glass sickness, iridescence, and
opalescence— Pontil marks—Sun-coloured glass

4 The Rest of the World   132

5 Bottles by Mail   136

Index   139

Acknowledgements

The bottles illustrated
on the cover are from
Joan Allen's stock at
the Collectors' Old Bottle
Room, 184 Main Road,
Biggin Hill, Kent, England.
The photograph was taken by
Jeremy McCabe of
Maidstone.

Readers familiar with the other titles in this series will know that my earlier book, *Bottle Collecting*, was written as a guide to the hobby in Great Britain. It examined in detail the methods used to find and to dig bottle dumps in the British Isles and it provided a brief outline of nineteenth century British bottle history together with information on methods used to date and how to clean the bottles found.

My aim in writing this book was to promote and encourage growth of the British bottle collecting hobby which at the time [1972] had only begun to cross the Atlantic from its birthplace in the United States. The book's popularity and the rapid growth of the British Bottle Collectors Club following its publication justify my claim to the achievement of that aim, though I do not doubt that bottle collecting would have become a major hobby in Britain with or without my book. It is a fascinating pastime; educational, profitable, and accessible to all regardless of age or sex. The book merely hurried its adoption from our cousins on the other side of the Atlantic, to whom all British collectors will be eternally grateful.

I was delighted and rather surprised by the book's reception in other parts of the world. Within a few weeks of its publication the British Bottle Collectors Club received hundreds of letters from the collectors in North America, Australia, New Zealand, and South Africa who had read *Bottle Collecting* and who were eager to trade with British diggers and buy bottles; to exchange historical information, and to swap yarns about site-hunting experiences. Soon the first letters had passed between British and overseas diggers, collectors and clubs; some weeks later parcels of bottles from Essex, England, from Wagga Wagga, New South Wales, from Auckland, New Zealand, from Port Elizabeth, South Africa, from Conroe, Texas, and from Montreal, Canada, were crossing the world's oceans. International bottle collecting was born.

Alas, those first, friendly letters were quickly followed by airmail threats and abuse. The Americans and Canadians accused the British of describing as rarities bottles fit only for five-and-ten-cent stores; the British told the Australians and New Zealanders that their bottles were in such poor condition that they were uncollectable; the Australians and New Zealanders hinted that the British were hanging on to their oldest bottles and shipping post-Victorian specimens Down Under. Only the South Africans seemed happy; but as they were by far the smallest contingent in the 'League of Bottle Collectors' nobody paid much attention to them. The rest of the bottle-collecting world abandoned inter-national trading and most collectors retreated to digging in their own backyards where they felt safe from eccentric foreigners who misunderstood the hobby.

One or two of those eccentrics—myself included—were not content to let matters rest at the unsatisfactory impasse. Why, I wondered, were the Americans with their extensive knowledge of bottle history unable to appreciate the rarity of a Rylands' Valve Codd? Where on earth did the Austra-lians and New Zealanders expect us to dig up eighteenth century bottles? Why were the bottles they sent to Britain in such sick condition with glass so clouded? And what did these foreigners mean by s.c.a., bimal, Maugham's Patent, and Hutchinson's? There was only one sure way to answer those questions: I would go and look for myself . . . .

Fortunately there is gypsy blood in my family. I have sisters, cousins, and half-forgotten great aunts scattered throughout the globe. I wrote to those whose addresses I could find and begged free bed and board in the interests of historical research, international peace-keeping, and my bank manager's sanity. From the United States, from Canada, from South Africa came offers of assistance; but my Australian relatives were lost in the outback and my letters were returned marked 'Gone away' or 'In jail'. There was only one thing for it. I squeezed an advance on royalties from my publisher and financed the Australian and New Zealand trips myself.

What follows are the results of a globe-trot around the

world's bottle dumps. I know now why many Australian bottles are oddly coloured—and what it's like to dig for bottles in temperatures over 100 deg. F. with deadly scorpions climbing up the digging tool! I know what a Maugham's Patent bottle looks like; I know why Canadians, Americans, South Africans, Australians, and New Zealanders find earlier nineteenth century bottles than British diggers even though the British have more unrecovered nineteenth century bottles beneath their feet than have all the other nations put together. I even understand terms such as s.c.a., open pontil, double ring seal, and BIMAL. I have become an international bottle collector and I have written this book to encourage all collectors in Britain, the United States, Canada, South Africa, Australia, and New Zealand to share my enthusiasm.

Within these pages I have described and illustrated the best-known bottles in all six countries and I have estimated each bottle's rarity and collector-value by comparison with similar bottles from other countries. The terminology used by each country's collectors is also explained and background information on site-hunting techniques, digging methods, cleaning, and bottle history is provided. In addition I have added notes on my own experiences when packaging, shipping, and mailing bottles to overseas countries in the hope that this information will help readers reduce risks of breakages and overcome problems with customs officials in the countries concerned. At the end of the book readers will also find a comprehensive address list of club dealers, collectors, books, and bottle magazines from which additional information on up-to-date bottle prices and current collecting trends can be obtained. Thus I have attempted to provide all the facts necessary for the successful re-birth of international bottle collecting in those English-speaking countries where the hobby already has large followings. In their bottle histories each has much in common with Britain—and other European countries—from which continent millions of bottles were exported in the eighteenth and nineteenth centuries. At the same time each country concerned has unique bottles which were manufactured locally to meet local needs, and it is these which provide individuality and make international bottle collecting such a fascinating subject.

Wherever in the world my interest in antique bottles has taken me I have met friendly folk who have readily provided assistance, advice, and hospitality. It seems the hobby attracts people like this and for that I am deeply grateful. I thank once again all who helped me put this book together, especially those on whom I depended heavily during my travels. I hope the contents of this book will help them as much as they helped me.

Take a map of Britain and draw on it a straight line from the tip of Cornwall in the south-west of England to New-castle-on-Tyne on the north-east coast. That line represents the 'frontier' of bottle collecting in Britain in 1975. More than ninety per cent of the nation's diggers and collectors live in the area east of that line, and within it there are approximately 30,000 enthusiasts of whom, it is estimated, some 10,000 are active dump diggers.

This concentration of a large number of diggers in a relatively small area of land is the first striking difference between the British bottle collecting scene and the situation in Australia and, to a lesser degree, in North America. In Australia, the United States, and Canada diggers and collectors are fairly evenly spread and dumps in all states are currently being excavated. In the British Isles, on the other hand, most of Wales and all of Scotland and Ireland are unexplored bottle-hunting territories if one discounts the handful of 'frontiersmen' who have ventured into these areas and the few isolated diggers who live west of the line.

This situation has very marked effects on the hobby within the British Isles. It explains the present shortage in Britain of some varieties of antique bottles; it accounts for the abundance of and interest in other types; and it is an important factor in the planning and carrying out of group activities within the British Bottle Collectors Club. Before discussing these subjects in detail let me explain how the situation arose and why it is unlikely to change for several years unless there is a marked growth in international bottle trading between Britain and other countries.

Quite by chance British bottle collecting began in the counties of Essex and Kent in the south-east part of the country. The first collectors happened to live in these two counties and, of course, they concentrated their digging activities on local dumps. They had little difficulty in finding suitable sites because vast areas of marshland on the banks of the Thames in Essex and the Medway in Kent were used during the nineteenth century as convenient dumping grounds for much of London's household refuse. Thousands of acres of marshland were reclaimed within the two counties by raising the level of land along the riverbanks with millions of unwanted bottles, pipes, pot lids, and other household throwaways. Once reclaimed some of this land was used for industrial sites—the Ford Motor Works at Dagenham sits on top of a vast Victorian dump—but most of it became grazing land for sheep and cattle, a use to which it is put to this day.

In spite of these wide open spaces flanking their tidal rivers, Essex and Kent are two of Britain's most densely populated counties. Consequently, it was not long before the successes of those early diggers attracted the attention of equally adventurous spirits living nearby. There were so many available sites on which to dig that the newcomers were easily absorbed even though their numbers soon ran into thousands. During the years 1970–72 every collector in Essex and Kent could obtain all the specimens he or she required simply by strolling along the foreshores of local creeks and rivers and picking up the bottles, pipes, pot lids, and other collectables washed out of the banks by the previous high tide. Pickings are much leaner nowadays; it is necessary to dig a few feet into the ground to make finds, but there is as yet no shortage of excellent sites in these two counties.

In other counties bordering London—Hertfordshire, Middlesex, Surrey, and Buckinghamshire—newcomers to the hobby were able to locate equally productive dumps along the banks of canals connected to the Thames. These man-made waterways also played an important role in the disposal of nineteenth century London's refuse; barges carried thousands of loads to disused claypits along their banks when the volume of refuse became too great to be absorbed by marshland reclamation schemes. In this way anyone living within the Greater London area, in which at least 10,000 of Britain's bottle collectors live, was

14

adequately provided with excellent dumps within twenty miles of home.

Since 1972 bottle collecting has spread northwards and westwards from London to all the heavily populated areas east of the imaginary line mentioned at the beginning of this chapter. Growth has been confined to this area mainly because it is the most densely urbanized part of the British Isles with large numbers of easily accessible nineteenth century refuse sites along canal banks, on coastal marshes, or in disused quarries and claypits. The geography of Britain is such that much of the land west of our imaginary line is occupied by mountains, moors and farmland. There *are* major cities—including Edinburgh, Glasgow, Dublin, and Belfast—but there is nothing comparable to the vast urban and industrial sprawls east of the line. As experienced dump diggers throughout the world will know, quite different techniques are used to locate bottle dumps in sparsely populated areas than are used to find sites near large towns. No doubt they will also understand the reluctance on the part of British diggers to leave the 'rich pickings' east of the line to go in search of isolated village and farm dumps further west.

That the small number of large towns and cities in the west have accessible and highly productive dumps has been confirmed by the few diggers who have yet explored them. Superb collections of bottles rated extremely rare in Britain have been found by quite inexperienced diggers in Scotland and Ireland; but these finds have not yet attracted southern and eastern diggers in sufficient numbers to generate widespread local interest in bottle collecting in cities such as Edinburgh, Glasgow, Dublin, and Belfast.

In the United States, Canada, and Australia it is not uncommon for weekend dump diggers to travel several hundred miles to an interesting bottle site. Such journeys are rare in Britain where congested roads, high fuel costs, and—of more importance—the availability of excellent local sites tend to deter even the more adventurous digger

15

from travelling further than twenty miles from his home-town to hunt bottles. As in other countries, bottle collecting is a family hobby in Britain. The average digger planning a Sunday bottle hunt is much more likely to think of the local site 'down the road' where he is assured of good finds and where he knows he and his wife and kids will meet most fellow-enthusiasts in the area than he is to contem-plate an uncertain journey to a little-known site fifty miles away. He regards his weekend dig as a social event where digging quite often takes second place to discussions on such topics as recent finds, the current prices of pot lids, or the latest article in *Bottles and Relics News*. Indeed, it is generally true to say of the British scene that the weekend dig is equivalent to the American or Australian bottle show. A substantial amount of bottle trading takes place on sites and it is not uncommon for collectors to bring along their latest acquisitions to be admired by other diggers. Prizes are *not* awarded to those who happen to have the best finds of the week; but otherwise these events are reminiscent of local bottle meets in California or New South Wales.

The British do not go in for organized bottle shows and conventions with the same enthusiasm shown by their overseas cousins. However, there is a national club, the British Bottle Collectors Club, sponsored by the country's largest bottle manufacturer and with a membership in-cluding almost every collector and digger in the country. The B.B.C.C. does a first-class job of organizing digging activities and collating historical information for publica-tion in the club's monthly magazine, *Bottles and Relics News*. From its national headquarters in Essex the B.B.C.C. arranges group digs in all of the counties east of the 'frontier' line. A local secretary in each county first contacts the land-owner on whose property a dump has been located in order to obtain permission for a club dig. If permission is granted a suitable date is decided upon and an announce-ment published in *Bottles and Relics News*. Each club member is pledged by acceptance of club rules to report to the local secretary details of all finds made. The secretary records a description of each find—type of bottle, embossing, colour, etc.—on a card which he sends to B.B.C.C. headquarters where it is added to a master file. In this way a complete record of finds made in Britain is being built up by the club; an invaluable reference source for all members interested in bottle history.

It is the B.B.C.C.'s success at locating sites and obtaining permission for digs from landowners and local government officials which makes club membership so beneficial to the average weekend digger with little time to devote to site hunting. On the other hand, it is the necessity to concentrate its energy on arranging hundreds of digs every year in those areas where membership is greatest which prevents the club opening up new bottle-digging territories in those parts of Britain where the hobby is still almost unknown.

A similar problem confronts the editorial staff of *Bottles and Relics News*. The majority of the magazine's readers acquire their bottles, whether purchased or dug, from sites where refuse was dumped during the period 1870–95. Because of these similarities in the ages and contents of British dumps now being dug the magazine's readers find and collect bottles which, apart from embossing, are similar no matter where they come from within the area of the hobby's present popularity. It is these bottles readers want to learn more about when they open their copies of the magazine each month; not about unusual bottles which might lie in far-away sites unlikely to be visited until all local dumps are exhausted. Hence a large number of articles in the magazine are devoted to well-known types of bottles.

The foregoing description of the British scene—thousands of diggers at work on similarly dated late Victorian dumps in the southern and eastern areas of the country—is of course a generalization which disregards a few hundred 'go-anywhere-dig-anything' professional bottle hunters and a handful of Scottish and Irish collectors living in Glasgow,

Edinburgh, Belfast, and Dublin. However, as far as overseas readers are concerned, there are no dangers in accepting my generalization as accurate. To explain why all those hard-working diggers have so far failed to recover large numbers of bottles dated earlier than 1870 I must give a brief account of refuse disposal methods used in Britain in the nineteenth century.

During the period of major gold strikes, in the United States and Australia (1849–70) when many of the bottles most prized today by collectors in those countries were being thrown into makeshift dumps in and around mining towns, Britain's major cities could already boast of their efficient refuse disposal schemes. As early as 1830 a regular and free collection service was provided by the Corporation of London and most large towns had similar services by 1840.

Empty bottles, jars, pots, household junk, and—most important of all—vast quantities of coal ash were collected from private houses by corporation dustmen and taken to large depots in each town. In London the depot was on the banks of the Thames at Lett's Wharf close to Blackfriars Bridge. Here teams of men and women employed as scavengers waded waist deep in the mountain of refuse and carefully sorted its contents. Empty bottles were sold to brewers, wine merchants, and mineral water makers; bones went to glue factories; broken pottery was purchased by roadmakers; and the coal ash was quickly bought by brickmakers who used it mixed with clay to make common bricks. The small amount of unsaleable material—offal and the like—was burned at the depot.

The revenue gained by the local corporation from the sale of sorted refuse not only paid the wages of dustmen and scavengers, but also resulted in a handsome profit which went into the city's coffers and was used to finance other services including the running of local workhouses for the poor.

Shortly after 1870 there occurred in Britain a major

recession in the brickmaking industry which severely reduced demand for ashes to make common bricks. Most corporations were then unable to sell the coal ashes which made up the bulk of collected refuse. In London the scavengers' wages were reduced to one halfpenny per day, but even then the refuse could not be sorted economically because the amount of ashes produced by the fast-expanding city increased almost daily. In desperation many corporations persuaded brickmakers to accept unsorted refuse free of charge. This scheme worked reasonably well until about 1875, particularly in the counties of Kent and Northamptonshire where there were large numbers of brickyards and hundreds of clay holes where bottles, pipes, pot lids, and other unwanted material could be dumped after the brickmakers had screened the refuse to extract ashes which they stockpiled during the recession.

At some brickyards dumps were set alight to deter plagues of rats and cockroaches which infested them. Contemporary newspapers in Kent and Northamptonshire carried numerous letters of complaint from people who lived close to dumps and whose lives were made miserable by these pests and by the stench of burning refuse.

Little was done to relieve their sufferings until about 1875 when the first large-scale marshland reclamation schemes were tried along the Thames foreshore near Barking Creek in Essex. The idea came from Holland and it was Dutch engineers who helped to make the project so successful. Within a few years all the refuse produced by the sprawling London metropolis was being carried by barges to the Essex marshes. Land reclamation projects became as popular as canal cutting had been in the previous century. Throughout the industrialized and densely populated areas of England every large town situated reasonably close to coastal or riverside marshes adopted London's method of ridding itself of unwanted refuse. Those towns without marshes nearby reclaimed the thousands of clay pits which had been dug along canal routes in the eighteenth century to obtain clay to line the bottoms of these man-made waterways. Once reclaimed by dumping some of the sites were transformed to public parks and recreation areas; but the majority were left untouched—until bottle hunters rediscovered them a few years ago.

It is worth noting that refuse disposal by dumping on land liable to flooding is still used in Britain, particularly in Essex and Kent where the first schemes were carried out. Many rich Victorian dumps have been lost in recent years before diggers could get to them by the dumping of vast amounts of modern garbage on top of the earlier material.

Visitors to London who wish to see evidence of the city's mid-Victorian refuse disposal methods need look no further than the slum clearance projects now taking place in London's East End where row-upon-row of Victorian terraces are being pulled down to make way for those modern cubes of concrete called housing units. Wander around one of these demolition sites and examine some of the common bricks torn from old house walls. Fragments of clay tobacco pipes, coloured pot lids, and black glass are easily spotted in the bricks—remnants of broken items overlooked by the unfortunate scavengers of Dickensian London.

Refuse collection services financed by sale of refuse can only succeed when there is sufficient refuse to make the project economically viable. This is equally true of reclamation projects: they cannot be attempted when the available refuse amounts to one cartload per week. Consequently neither of these methods was used in small towns, villages and rural areas of Britain during the nineteenth century. On farms and country estates refuse was often simply ploughed into the land as fertilizer. In villages and small towns it was dumped in any convenient hole which could be easily reached by all residents and then it was covered with a few feet of soil to provide new land for crops. No doubt many bottles were saved and re-used several times in country districts during the early nineteenth century; but mass production and the new designs and shapes of bottles which came in ever-increasing varieties after 1840 soon encouraged even country folk to relegate their old bottles to the local dump. It is on these sites, the majority of which have yet to be explored because they lie beyond the 'frontier', that onion bottles, sealed case gins, early bitters and cures, open pontil specimens, and many hitherto unrecorded pot lids will be found when Britain's dump diggers are persuaded to forsake larger and more productive late Victorian sites in heavily populated areas.

Mineral waters. It was a fortunate coincidence that sorting and re-use of refuse ceased in Britain at a time when some of the most interesting mineral water bottles first appeared. Hiram Codd of Camberwell, Surrey, perfected his globe-stoppered bottle in 1872. Within two years Codd had sold manufacturing licences to several glass bottle makers and Codd's 'Original' quickly became popular in the soft drinks trade. Prior to its introduction mineral waters were bottled either in pointed-bottomed Hamilton's or in cylindrical stoneware bottles with cork closures. The Hamilton competed with its globe-stoppered rival until the turn-of-the-century; but its wired-on cork and the difficulties its shape presented to bottle fillers and to shopkeepers, who had to store it horizontally on their shelves to keep the cork moist and to prevent escape of gas, caused it to be used by fewer and fewer mineral water makers throughout this period. Hamilton bottles enjoyed two brief revivals of popularity. The first occurred in the 1880's when coloured Hamilton's—dark green, cobalt blue, brown, and amber—were introduced. The second took place in the 1890's when the improved Hamilton with a round instead of a pointed bottom was introduced in response to requests from mineral water makers for a Hamilton that was easier to handle when being filled and corked. Large numbers of these improved Hamilton's, most of which were used by companies in Belfast including Cantrell & Cochrane and

Bottles found

21

Ross, found their way to North America and Australia as ships' ballast when they fell out of use following the adoption of screw-stoppered bottles by these companies. A flat-bottomed Hamilton was introduced at about the same time.

Stoneware bottles with incised trade marks continued in use throughout the nineteenth century, though after 1872 they were only used in the mineral water trade for ginger beer. Transfer-printed varieties were used in Britain as late as 1930.

One of the glassmakers who took out a licence to manufacture Codd's 'Original' was Ben Rylands of Barnsley, Yorks. Ben was a perfectionist and from the outset he endeavoured to make his products of the highest quality. The manufacture of globe-stoppered bottles required strong glass and precision moulding in order to produce a bottle which would withstand constant re-filling and with a closure which remained gas-tight throughout the bottle's working life. Ben Rylands' success at making such bottles secured for his company a large share of the globe-stoppered bottle market. By 1878 he was Britain's largest manufacturer of these bottles and in that year he took Hiram Codd into partnership.

The two worked very well together. Codd developed several improvements to his 'Original' bottle including the 'Bulb' with bulbous shoulders which acted as traps for the stopper during pouring; and the 'Empress' with sloping shoulder indentations which caused the globe stopper to roll to one side of the bottle during cleaning. He also greatly improved the tools used in the bottle-making process to form the neck indentations and the groove which held the sealing ring.

In 1881 Ben Rylands died and his son Dan inherited his share of the Codd-Rylands partnership. Like Hiram Codd, Dan Rylands was a clever inventor, but the two men found it almost impossible to work together. Their rivalry as inventors resulted in constant friction and disagreement, though between them they did develop a number of

Fig. I Brown and pale amber Codds from Britain

improvements to the globe-stoppered bottle including the 'Reliance' which could be inclined left or right during pouring.

By mutual agreement they dissolved their partnership in 1884. Codd returned to Camberwell where he set up as a bottle manufacturer and also tried several other ventures with little success. Dan Rylands, now free to exploit his own inventive genius, continued to improve his bottles. In 1886 he produced the 'Acme', similar to the 'Reliance' but with two safety indents to hold the stopper when the bottle was brushed during cleaning. Around 1887 he perfected his unique 'Valve' bottle with a glass plunger in its shoulder which was pressed to relieve gas pressure and open the bottle. At about the same time he patented the use of coloured lips on bottles—blue, amber, red, and dark green —as a means of identification to deter the widespread practice among mineral water makers of stealing bottles belonging to rival companies. Rylands used the coloured lips on all variations of his globe-stoppered bottles and

23

advertised them widely in the mineral water trade press. In his advertisements he undertook not to sell bottles with the same coloured lips to two mineral water makers in the same town. Although a clever idea, this method of identifying bottles was not a success in the south-east of England where there were far too many small mineral water companies in close and fierce competition and where Dan Rylands was unable to guarantee that the territories of firms using the same coloured lips would not overlap. However, the idea was quite successful in northern England and much used in the colonies including Australia, New Zealand, and South Africa.

In 1888, a year after the introduction of Dan Rylands' coloured lip bottles, patent protection on Codd's 'Original' bottle lapsed. This meant that any bottle maker could now produce them without a licence from the inventor. As a result Dan Rylands faced stiff competition from other bottle makers who not only produced aqua versions of Codd's 'Original', but who also made coloured varieties to compete with Rylands' coloured lips. Some makers of Hamilton bottles also adopted coloured glass at about this time.

Even fiercer competition came from other inventors who produced a variety of internally stopped bottles for mineral water makers. These included the Barrett and Elers' 'Wooden Plug', which was in fact patented in 1871, a year earlier than Codd's 'Original', and which captured a fair share of the colonial market from that date. Sykes-Magvay, Cannington-Shaw, Kilner Brothers, Barnett and Foster, Breffit, Lamont, Valet, and Sutcliffe were some of the bottle makers who invented alternative closures or turned out Codd's 'Original' during this period. The alternatives included bottles with oval, disc-shaped, and plug stoppers which employed dozens of different methods to trap the internal stopper during pouring of the contents. Some had indents at the base of the bottle; some had a deep groove in the middle of the body; others used lead-weighted

Fig. 2
Left. An early Codd made by Ben Rylands
Right. A Codd made after 1885 by Dan Rylands

stoppers which sank on opening. Most took a slice of Rylands' market and because Dan Rylands had devoted most of his factory's manufacturing capacity to globe-stoppered bottles he was soon in financial difficulties. When the massive swing to screw stoppers came at the beginning of the twentieth century Dan Rylands was one of the first makers of internally stoppered bottles to go out of business.

The foregoing summary of mineral water bottles made in Britain during the late nineteenth century gives some idea of the many varieties found by diggers. Most of the bottle makers and the vast majority of firms that used them were located in that part of Britain where bottle collecting is now a popular hobby and where late Victorian dumps contain large numbers of specimens. There are thousands of mineral waters enthusiasts throughout the country who devote their entire collections to these bottles. I have also seen outstanding collections in Australia, New Zealand,

Fig. 3 These bottles c contained natural min waters bottled at a Bri health resort in the nineteenth century

and South Africa where British bottle makers found excellent markets for their products throughout the nineteenth century. Many Australian collections include rare examples of Rylands' coloured lips and other choice specimens which sold well on the export market.

At the present time there is little interest in British-made internally stoppered bottles in the United States where the majority of mineral and soda water bottle collectors concentrate on bottles with Hutchinson stoppers which dominated the American market in the late nineteenth century. Most Americans refer to these bottles as 'Codds' whether or not they were invented or made by that gentleman, and few Americans are aware that there are more variations in British mineral water bottle closures than there are in American fruit jars. There can be no doubt that most British mineral waters enthusiasts would be delighted to trade some of their internally stoppered bottles for examples of American Hutchinson's and other sodas if collectors in the United States showed more interest in British 'Codds'.

NOTES ON RARITY

Codd-Hamilton hybrids. Several bottle makers who were turning out pointed Hamilton's when Hiram Codd began issuing licences for his 'Original' after 1872 reduced the cost of making moulds for the new bottle by using the body mould of a Hamilton when blowing a Codd. This produced the Codd-Hamilton hybrid, an oddity eagerly sought by present-day collectors. Its globe-stoppered top rendered the pointed bottom obsolete because it was unnecessary to store Codd's bottle horizontally. Rating: Very rare. Price guide: 50.

Rylands' 'Valve'. Rating: Very rare. Price guide: 60.
Rylands' coloured lips. Rating (on 'Original', 'Bulb',

27

Fig. 4 (*Above*) Dumpy soda water bottles in dark green glass. From a British dump dated 1890

Fig. 5 British mineral waters bottles with internal screw stoppers

28

'Empress', 'Acme', and 'Reliance'): Rare. Price guide: 40.

(on 'Valve') Rating: Very rare. Price guide: 70.

(on Codd-Hamilton hybrid) Rating: Very rare: Price guide: 60.

Coloured Codd's 'Original' (dark green). Rating: Difficult to find. Price guide: 30.

(brown) Rating: Harder to find. Price guide: 40.

(blue) Rating: Very rare. Price guide: 50.

Coloured Hamilton. As above.

Internally stoppered bottles not made by Codd or Rylands. Rating: Not common. Price guide: 20+.

Codd 'Original' in aqua. Rating: Common. Price guide: Less than 1.

> *Exceptions:* Embossed BEN RYLANDS. Rating: Rare. Price guide 40.
>
> Embossed RYLANDS & CODD. Rating: Rare. Price guide: 30.

Hamilton in aqua. Rating: Common. Price guide: 1.

Stoneware ginger beer, incised or transfer-printed. Rating: Common. Price guide: 1.

Note: It is known that Hiram Codd took out a patent for the manufacture of a stoneware globe-stoppered bottle. No complete specimens have ever been found, but there are unconfirmed reports of diggers finding fragments.

Inks. Britain's late Victorian dumps hold a rich assortment of glass and stoneware ink bottles. When the site is dated earlier than 1895 almost all of the glass inks have crude sheared lips and the stoneware is of a pale to very dark-brown, salt-glazed texture. In dumps dated later than 1895 many of the glass inks have machine-finished lips with mould seams out of line with body seams, as seen on early twentieth century American bottles made on Owens machines. The stoneware in these dumps is often cream or white in colour.

The commonest glass ink is undoubtedly the eight-sided sheared lipped aqua type which is found in all sizes from one-and-a-half to three inches in height. Almost as common is the aqua boat which varies in both length and height from two to four inches. Ribbed squares come next in the common aqua varieties, closely followed by ribbed oblongs; both are found in similar dimensions to eight-siders. Much less common, though not too difficult to find in large numbers, are aqua bells with sheared lips. Dark green and cobalt blue specimens of all of these inks are scarce, and brown ones are very scarce indeed. Embossing other than glass makers' base markings is most uncommon on all British glass inks.

Specimens regarded as rarities in any colour by British diggers include cones, umbrellas, three-siders, barrels, teakettles, and igloos. (It should be noted that the ink British collectors call an igloo is of a domed shape with a *vertical* spout attached to its side.) Rarest and most prized of all British inks is the cottage which has embossed doors, windows, and roof tiles together with a chimney pot formed by the mouth of the bottle—a true figural ink and the only known British figural in this class of bottles. Only a handful of aqua specimens have been recovered. Stoneware cottage inks have also been found by a few fortunate diggers, but most of the small stoneware inks recovered are plain round specimens. The exception is a cone which usually has a dark brown salt-glazed finish.

Most of Britain's potteries made bulk ink containers in the nineteenth century and the majority placed an incised pottery mark on the bodies of their products. Bourne, Lovatt, Stephen Green, Port Dundas, Doulton & Watts, Doulton, and Stiff are some of the marks found on containers by British diggers.

American collectors to whom I have shown examples of common British glass inks have been fascinated by the crudity of their sheared lips which were left as sharp and as jagged as possible by bottlemakers so that the glass would cut into the cork stopper to form a leak-proof seal. British ink collectors are equally fascinated by American cones, umbrellas and Carter figurals so there is obviously a lot of scope for trans-Atlantic exchanges in this branch of bottle collecting.

Australian and New Zealand ink collectors will also find much to interest them from Britain even though inks generally found in those countries are similar to British shapes. Britain has fewer embossed examples but a much greater range of sizes and colour shades. The enormous variety of stoneware inks available to collectors will also appeal to Australians and New Zealanders.

NOTES ON RARITY

Eight-sided; aqua; sheared lip. Rating: Common. Price guide: Less than 1.

Boat; aqua; sheared lip. Rating: Common. Price guide: Less than 1.

Round; aqua; machine made. Rating: Common. Price guide: Less than 1.

Ribbed square; aqua; sheared lip. Rating: Common. Price guide: 1.

Ribbed oblong; aqua; sheared lip. Rating: Common. Price guide: 1.

Bell; aqua; sheared lip. Rating: Less common. Price guide: 3.

Coloured specimens of any of above:
(dark green) Rating: Uncommon. Price guide: 5.
(teal blue) Rating: Uncommon. Price guide: 15.
(cobalt blue) Rating: Very uncommon. Price guide: 20.

Embossed specimens of any of above. Rating: Very uncommon. Price guide: 10.

Cone; any colour; any lip. Rating: Rare. Price guide: 20

Umbrella; any colour; any lip. Rating: Rare. Price guide: 20.

Fig. 6
Two unusual inks f
Britain
Left. A pale blue igloo
Right. A three-sider c
plete with original c
stopper and wax seal

Fig. 7 Bulk inks in st
ware

Barrel; any colour; any lip. Rating: Rare. Price guide: 20.

Three-sider; any colour; any lip. Rating: Very rare. Price guide: 40.

Igloo; any colour; any lip. Rating: Very rare. Price guide: 30.

Teakettle; any colour; any lip. Rating: Very rare. Price guide: 40.

Cottage; any colour; any lip. Rating: Exceedingly rare. Price guide: 200.

Cottage; stoneware. Rating: Exceedingly rare. Price guide: 180.

Round; stoneware. Rating: Common. Price guide: Less than 1.

Bulk; stoneware; any size up to one gallon. Rating: Common. Price guide: 1.

Fig. 8 A British cottage ink

Bitters. Had I written this book two years ago I might have completed this section with a single sentence. 'There are no bitters bottles in Britain.' Certainly very few examples were found by those early diggers around London; but an increasing number now turning up as dumps in northern areas are being explored for the first time. Many of those recovered have come from dumps in North Wales and it seems probable there is some significance in this fact. Wales has long been associated with temperance movements; hard liquor was much frowned upon during the Victorian period in most Welsh counties and it is likely that bitters drinking was widely adopted as a more acceptable social habit.

For the benefit of British readers who know nothing of the bitters story I must explain that the sale of gin, whisky, and other alcoholic drinks disguised as medicines was practised in Europe, North America, Australia, and all British colonies in the eighteenth and nineteenth centuries. This was done both to avoid heavy taxes on liquor and as a defence against social reformers who attacked hard drinking as the great evil of the times. A few bitter-tasting herbs of doubtful medicinal properties were added to the spirits and the resulting brew, which got its name from its taste, was bottled and sold as a remedy for every complaint and malady likely to be found in a medical dictionary. (One company even claimed its bitters were a certain cure for lying!) The only remnant of the bitters drinking habit which survives in Britain today is the practice of ordering pink gins in saloon bars. The 'pink' is angostura bitters, a south American herb once used as a medicine.

Of the four bitters bottles which have turned up in significant numbers in Welsh dumps during recent years two are of German origin, one is British, and the fourth is an American bottle known to be a rare find in the United States. The German specimens are an olive green bottle embossed 'bitterquell' on its base, and a milk glass bottle of case gin shape embossed 'Hartwig Kantorowicz'. The British specimen is a black glass cylindrical three-piece mould bottle embossed 'Kent Hop Bitters'.

Most interesting of the four is the American specimen, a black glass Dr. Soule's Hop Bitters identical in all respects, with the exception of the doctor's name, to the well-known American bottle used by Dr. Doyle.

That many more bitters bottles await discovery in un-explored British dumps, in particular those in Wales and also in Scotland where temperance societies were equally powerful in the nineteenth century, is attested by the number of bitters advertised in contemporary British newspapers. These include Dr. Siegert's Angostura Bitters, Pomegranate Bitters, Swain Boord's Orange Bitters, Dr. Ralay's Royal Digestive Bitters, Drake's Bitters, Hostetter's Bitters, Stoughton Bitters, Wolfe's Aromatic Bitters, Blankenheyn's Aromatic Bitters, American Cocktail Bitters, Lediard's Stomach Bitters, XLL Bitters, Meyer's Bitters, Gauly's Baltimore Bitters, John Jaap's Bitters, Birresbon Mineral Water Bitters, and Pomeranza Bitters.

NOTES ON RARITY

All bitters bottles are rare finds in Britain at the present time, but because so few examples have come to light there is no great interest in collecting them. Most British diggers are unaware of the almost fanatical interest in bitters bottles in the United States and I advise American collectors seeking British-found specimens to offer other types of bottles as exchanges. There are few British collectors who would not trade one of their bitters, however rare, for a Carter's figural ink or a fire grenade. This situation could change if dumps in Britain's unexplored regions prove exceptionally rich in varieties of bitters bottles in which case British collectors are likely to take a greater interest in them.

Sealed bottles. American and Australian dump diggers will be surprised to learn that even those British diggers who confine their activities to dumps dated 1875–95 can confidently expect to find three or four sealed bottles during a year of weekend digging. In the United States, and in Australia if one discounts Dutch case gins, sealed bottles are only found in dumps dated earlier than 1860. In Britain the practice of impressing brand names and trade marks into pads of red-hot glass on the shoulders or bodies of bottles as an alternative to (or in addition to) labels and embossing did not die out completely until about 1895.

The late Victorian seals are quite different to the seventeenth, eighteenth, and early nineteenth century sealed bottles which were onion shaped or squat cylindrical bottles with string rings beneath their lips. Almost all of those early bottles carried seals impressed with the initials or family crest of the bottle's owner and, occasionally, the date when the bottle was made. Late nineteenth century seals usually bear the trade marks of whisky distillers, wine merchants or breweries. Although black glass specimens are known, the majority are green (olive to aqua) and all have applied lips. Some are turn-moulds and a fair number are of three-piece mould design. The seal is usually placed on the shoulder of the bottle, though some of the beers have body seals. About half of the one hundred or so varieties so far recovered are of Continental origin, French and German specimens being rather more common than bottles from other countries. All contained alcoholic beverages of one form or another.

There are many sealed bottle enthusiasts in Britain and there is one group of seals which attracts more collector interest than any other. This is the Zara group. Collectors in the United States and Canada will be familiar with twentieth century Luxardo figural decanters in glass and ceramics which, before being emptied and proudly displayed on collectors' shelves, contain maraschino liqueur. The Zara sealed bottles found in Britain are the forerunners of these decanters. They were used in the nineteenth century by liqueur makers in Zara when that city was the capital of Dalmatia and part of the Austrian Empire. Slender and very beautiful bottles, they range in colour from aquamarine to emerald and are to be found in both square and round varieties. All have large shoulder seals bearing the spread-eagle emblem of the Austrian Empire together with the word 'Zara' and the name of the liqueur maker. Those used by the Drioli family are the oldest and have sheared and re-annealed lips reminiscent of American historical flasks. Later and less frequently found specimens have applied lips and names including Magazzin and Luxardo.

Another group of highly prized late Victorian sealed bottles is that which includes body-sealed beers. Cylindrical bottles in black, amber, or aqua glass, they have large body seals bearing the words, 'One Imperial Pint'. More than a dozen different types have been found.

There can be no doubt that thousands of eighteenth and early nineteenth century sealed bottles will be found when dumps in remote regions of Britain are fully explored.

Fig. 9 Zara sealed bottles from a British dump dated 1885

Superb specimens in black glass and with crude pontil marks have already been dug up near abandoned lead mines in the mountains of Wales and along the tracks of a disused railway line in Yorkshire. Others have come to light in the cellars of derelict houses in North West England. In Scotland and Ireland there are thousands of overgrown crofts and smallholdings abandoned when their tenants were forced to emigrate to America and Australia in the early years of the previous century at a time when sealed bottles were in common use. Each of those sites has a tiny unexplored dump somewhere nearby awaiting the attention of British bottle hunters at present preoccupied with sites further south. Overseas collectors eager to acquire some of those prized specimens should either visit Britain and take digging holidays in those regions or encourage more British diggers to seek them by offering to trade rare inks and coloured mineral water bottles for them.

NOTES ON RARITY

Continental seal. Turn mould; aqua or shades of green. Rating: Uncommon. Price guide: 40.

Turn mould; black glass. Rating: Uncommon. Price guide: 50.

Fig. 10 (*Above*) A n nineteenth century Brit sealed bottle

Fig. 11 (*Left*) An eightee century sealed bottle fr Britain

Fig. 12 (*Facing right*) British sealed bottle da 1887

Beer. Two or three-mould; aqua; body seal. Rating: Uncommon. Price guide: 50.

Two or three-mould; black glass; body seal. Rating: Uncommon. Price guide: 60.

Zara seal. Drioli; sheared lip. Rating: Uncommon. Price guide: 50.

Other maker; applied lip. Rating: Rare. Price guide: 60.

British seal. Turn mould; aqua or shades of green. Rating: Uncommon. Price guide: 50.

Turn mould; black glass. Rating: Uncommon. Price guide: 60.

Two or three-mould; aqua or shades of green. Rating: Uncommon. Price guide: 60.

Two or three-mould; black glass. Rating: Very uncommon. Price guide: 70.

Free-blown seal. Cylindrical; black or olive glass; rough pontil. Rating: Very rare. Price guide: 150.

Onion; black or olive glass; rough pontil. Rating: Extremely rare. Price guide: 200.

Case gins and Schnapps. For the greater part of the nineteenth century gin was the most popular hard liquor in Britain. It was the drink of the working classes (the rich preferred brandy and port) and rivers of the stuff were consumed in the gin palaces of London's East End and in other large cities where life was often so wretched it could only be tolerated when seen through a gin bottle-darkly. The dumps around London bear witness to the former popularity of 'mothers' ruin'. They are amply stocked with beautiful wide-shouldered, tapering, olive-green case gin bottles—alas, hardly any of them bearing a shoulder seal or even embossing to enlighten today's collectors about their histories. Considering the rich assortment of sealed case gins to be found in the colonial dumps of Australia, New Zealand, and South Africa, it is difficult to account for the lack of sealed specimens in British dumps. It may be that unsealed British examples were made in Britain and filled with English gin, though contemporary bottle makers' catalogues do not show illustrations of case bottles in their lists of standard products. Newspapers of the day carried many advertisements for Geneva and Schnapps which suggests that the case gins British diggers find are indeed of Dutch origin. Perhaps Holland's gin makers used paper labels on bottles for the nearby British market at a much earlier date than they did on bottles which were to be sent on long sea voyages during which there was a great risk of paper labels becoming wet and falling off before the bottles reached their destinations. Whatever the explanation it is a sad fact that only one in one thousand case gins found in Britain carries a shoulder seal. Almost without exception the seals are the familiar AVH of the A. van Hoboken Company, a very well-known sealed case gin to diggers in Australia.

Large numbers of Schnapps bottles are found on sites throughout the country and the traditional shape of this straight-sided smokey-green specimen is well-known to British diggers. Proof of Dutch origin is revealed in the single word SCHIEDAM embossed on one side of almost every specimen found. Miniature examples four inches tall and with the same embossing occasionally turn up.

NOTES ON RARITY

The rarity of sealed case gins in Britain offers excellent prospects for collectors in Australia where these bottles are quite common. Most British collectors would be delighted to trade rare internally-stoppered mineral water for good sealed gins.

Case gin. Dark green; shoulder seal. Rating: Very rare.

Price guide: 60.
Dark green; no seal. Rating: Very common. Price guide: 10.

Schnapps. Dark green; embossed SCHIEDAM. Rating: Common. Price guide: 10.

Dark green; miniature; embossed SCHIEDAM. Rating: Rare. Price guide: 30.

Black glass. Although the widespread use of black glass died out in Britain shortly after 1880 just as it did in the United States and elsewhere, many whisky distillers and some brewers continued to use them well into the 1890's. Black whiskies with applied lips and cork closures provide collectors with a range of bottle shapes. In addition to richly embossed cylindrical bottles with lady's leg necks, there are many broad, dumpy bottles used by both Scotch and Irish distillers to be found in British dumps. Some are of three-piece mould design and those embossed with pictorial trade marks are very popular collectors' items. Square and oblong black glass whisky bottles are also widely collected, the prize specimen being a square Thorne's whisky which also has a shoulder seal. Strap-sided coffin flasks are occasionally found; pumpkin seeds in black glass are unknown.

The beer bottles offer no variety of shape; all are of two or three-mould cylindrical shape with internal screw stoppers. Nevertheless they are eagerly collected for their deep and ornate embossed trade marks which include animals, birds, human figures, steam engines, ships, and one prized specimen showing a penny-farthing bicycle. Most are available in half-pint, pint, and quart sizes.

Rarest of all the embossed black glass bottles are dumpy, blob-top ginger beers identical in size and shape to common stoneware ginger beers. They are made from exceptionally thick glass which gives them an almost true opaque blackness. No matter what the conditions in dumps which

Fig. 13 Black glass gin beers

contain them they all come up in shining, mint condition. Less than a dozen ginger beer makers are known to have used these much sought-after glass bottles.

Many turn-mould black glass wines with deep kick-ups are also found in British dumps. Most are of Continental origin and, although quite attractive, they are not widely collected because, being turn-moulds, they lack embossing. The few labelled specimens recovered from old cellars are of course highly prized.

Fig. 14 A black glass whisky bottle from a Scottish dump

NOTES ON RARITY

Those black glass whisky bottles used by large distilleries are fairly common in Britain; overseas collectors should have no difficulty in acquiring specimens. Bottles used by little-known distilleries are more difficult to find and are also in demand with Britain's black glass collectors. Beer bottles embossed with the names and trade marks of local companies are usually of little interest to foreign collectors. Nevertheless, I urge overseas readers to seek specimens of Britain's pictorially embossed black glass beers if they wish to own superb examples of embossing craftsmanship. Australian collectors, who tend to regard all internal screw

42

bottles as modern, should note that in Britain almost all of these heavily embossed black glass beers were made before 1900.

Whisky. Two or three-mould; applied lip; from well-known distilleries. Rating: Fairly common. Price guide: 15.
As above; from little-known distilleries. Rating: Harder to find. Price guide: 25.
Dumpy; applied lip. Rating: Uncommon. Price guide: 35.
Square or oblong; applied lip. Rating: Uncommon Price guide: 35.
Coffin flask; applied lip. Rating: Rare Price guide: 50.
Beer. Cylindrical; internal screw. Rating: Common. Price guide: 10.
Ginger beer. Dumpy; blob-top. Rating: Rare. Price guide: 60.
Wine. Turn-mould; applied lip; unembossed. Rating: Common. Price guide: 5.

Fig. 15 Typical late nineteenth century black glass beer bottle from Britain

Acid etched glass. The use of hydrofluoric acid to etch trade marks on the bodies of bottles was in Britain mainly confined to coloured soda water syphons made before 1890. The only other acid etched bottles to be found are coffin flasks and pumpkin seeds bearing the names of hotels or public houses and occasionally the name of the hotel keeper or publican. Those bearing names such as Swan, Eagle, Crown, or Royal Oak are common and in no great demand. Those bearing historical or unusual names such as Queen Victoria, Southern Cross, Mayflower, or Great Western Railway are eagerly collected. Several hundred variations are known.

Syphon. Coloured (blue, pink, dark green). Rating: Difficult to find. Price guide: 40.

Coffin flask. Aqua; applied lip; common name. Rating: Fairly common. Price guide: 10.

As above; uncommon name. Rating: In great demand. Price guide: 40.

Pumpkin seed. As above.

Blue glass. Britain's late Victorian dumps provide a range of bottles made from blue glass. Most common are ribbed poisons of half-ounce to twenty ounce capacity embossed NOT TO BE TAKEN. The majority of these are eight-sided or of oblong shape, though three and six-sided examples are turned up fairly often. Cylindrical cobalt blue castor oils with long necks are more difficult to find and embossed specimens in this group are unknown. The castor oils have applied lips which distinguish them from another group of similarly shaped blue bottles with jagged sheared lips called 'syrups bottles' by British collectors. They get their name from rare specimens embossed HALFPENNY SYRUPS which occasionally turn up—an accepted misnomer; all the embossed specimens found so far have been aqua!

Blue fire grenades are regarded as prized specimens, the only type found being Harden's round specimen with embossed star. Most of these have come from derelict hotels and old houses; those found in dumps are almost invariably broken. Perfect specimens of chemist's shop bottles in blue glass and with painted or enamelled gold labels are equally difficult to find in dumps, though excellent bottles of this type have been recovered from old cellars and storerooms.

The rarest dump find is undoubtedly a wedge-shaped bottle bearing an embossed registered design mark and the words PRICE'S PATENT CANDLE COMPANY. The bottle once contained glycerine and it is one of the most unusual and

Fig. 16 (*Left*) Price's Patent Candle Co. bottle. Wedge-shaped, cobalt blue glass

Fig. 17 (*Right*) A cobalt blue poison bottle from Britain. 20-oz capacity

attractive to be found in British dumps. (Note: Aqua specimens of this bottle have also been found. They are equally rare.) Less striking, though a similar shade of cobalt blue, is an oblong bottle embossed MEXICAN HAIR RENEWER, another prized dump find. The other blue glass bottles generally found in dumps have been covered in the inks and mineral waters sections above.

Fig. 18   A 2-oz poison bottle in cobalt blue glass

NOTES ON RARITY

Poison. Eight-sided or oblong; half-ounce to eight ounce capacity; embossed NOT TO BE TAKEN. Rating: Common. Price guide: 3.

As above; twelve- to twenty-ounce capacity. Rating: Common. Price guide: 5.

Three or six-sided; embossed NOT TO BE TAKEN; half-ounce to twenty-ounce capacity. Rating; Uncommon. Price guide: 10.

Castor oil. Cylindrical; applied lip; unembossed. Rating: Uncommon. Price guide: 15.

Syrups. Cylindrical; sheared lip; unembossed. Rating: Fairly common. Price guide: 5.

Fire grenade. Harden's Star. Rating: Rare. Price guide: 50.

Shop bottle. Cylindrical; painted or enamelled label. Rating: Difficult to find. Price guide: 25.

Price's Patent Candle Company. Wedge-shaped; applied lip; embossed registered design mark. Rating: Extremely rare. Price guide: 100.

Mexican Hair Renewer: Oblong; applied lip. Rating: Rare. Price guide: 40.

Patent medicines. Many of the best patent medicine bottles found in British dumps were used for American products sold in Britain during the late nineteenth century. These include Warner's Safe Cure, Warner's Safe Nervine, Radam's Microbe Killer, Dr. Townsend's Sarsaparilla, Dr. Kilmer's Swamp Root Kidney Cure, and several more. Bottles used for British patent medicines are generally less flamboyant in their embossed advertising claims and unlikely to be of great interest to overseas collectors. There *are* exceptions. One is the small violin-shaped bottle used for Robert Turlington's Balsam of Life. Another is True Daffy's Elixir.

The Turlington bottle is well-known in the United States where early examples made by American glassworks during the time when British supplies of this bottle— and its contents—were cut off during the War of Independence fetch high prices. Dr. Dyott, of Dyottville Glassworks fame, made copies of this British bottle as did several other American bottle makers throughout the nineteenth century. It should be noted that almost all of the examples found in British dumps are pontil marked.

The Daffy's Elixir bottle was also copied by Dr. Dyott but it does not seem to have been made in the United States after 1850. The complete wording on embossed

British specimens reads: DICEY & CO'S TRUE DAFFY'S ELIXIR. SEE THAT THE WORDS DICEY & CO ARE ON THE GOVT. STAMP OVER THE CORK.

NOTES ON RARITY

Overseas collectors should note that almost all British-made examples of American patent medicines differ in some way from those found in the United States and Australia. Warner's Safe Cure bottles have the word LONDON where American examples have ROCHESTER, N.Y. and Australian examples have MELBOURNE. British Warner's are also found in olive-green glass as well as in the more usual amber-brown; they are also often taller bottles than those found in America. Similarly, the British version of Radam's Microbe Killer has a slightly different neck and lip to the American specimens I have seen. Dr. Townsend's Sarsaparilla bottles are found with slightly different embossing: I have seen specimens with the additional words THE BLOOD PURIFIER embossed on one panel.

These bottles are enthusiastically collected in Britain and most collectors would be delighted to trade their swaps for examples of American and Australian examples of the same bottles. They would also be happy to trade for examples of some of America's more common patent medicines bearing flamboyant embossing. Several British olive-green Warner's Safe Cures have already crossed the Atlantic in exchange for specimens of the fairly common American aqua bottle embossed BUMSTEAD'S WORM SYRUP. ONE BOTTLE HAS KILLED 100 WORMS. CHILDREN CRY FOR MORE. JUST TRY IT.

Warner's Safe Cure, London. Amber-brown; applied lip; approx. 9½ ins. Rating: Scarce. Price guide: 40.
As above; approx. 11½ ins. Rating: Scarce. Price guide: 50.

Olive green; applied lip; approx. 9½ ins. Rating: Scarce. Price guide: 50.

As above; approx. 11½ ins Rating: Rare. Price guide: 60.

Warner's Safe Nervine, London. As above.

Radam's Microbe Killer. Amber; re-annealed sheared lip. Rating: Rare. Price guide: 80.

Dr. Townsend's Sarsaparilla. Aqua; sheared lip. Rating: Scarce. Price guide: 30.

Aqua; sheared lip; embossed THE BLOOD PURIFIER. Rating: Rare. Price guide: 50.

Dr. Kilmer's Swamp Root. Kidney Cure. Aqua; sheared lip. Rating: Scarce. Price guide: 30.

Turlington. Aqua; violin-shaped; pontil. Rating: Rare. Price guide: 50.

Daffy's Elixir. Aqua; oblong; applied lip. Rating: Rare. Price guide: 80.

Fig. 19 Two dark gr
Warner's bottles f
London. The bottle on
right is a rare two-
specimen

48

Fig. 20   Daffy's   Elixir
bottle

Stoneware. There can be no doubt that Britain has a much
wider range of stoneware bottles than any of the other
countries covered in this book. Estimates of the number of
different trade marks either transfer-printed or incised on
British ginger beers alone vary in quantity between 5,000
and 10,000—figures which do not include the varieties yet
to be found in Scotland and Ireland where stoneware
bottles were even more widely used than they were in
England! Yet in spite of their profusion these bottles are
eagerly collected. Competition between ginger beer fans
to obtain specimens with picturesque underglaze transfers
is keen. Whenever a new dump containing these bottles is
opened up the ginger beer collectors are always among the
first to dig deep in the hope of finding unrecorded varieties
or some of the rarer two-tone bottles with coloured
shoulders and necks.

Blacking pots with wide-flared mouths form the next
largest stoneware group. Few are transfer-printed; the
majority carry only an incised pottery mark and their
colours range from dense black to pure white. Bulk ink

Fig. 21   Transfer-print
ginger beers

containers are almost as common, as are the thousands of
miscellaneous pots, bottles and jars used for all manner of
products including fish paste, meat paste, mustard, furniture
polish, varnish, essence, mayonnaise, liquid soap, bleach,
jam, clotted cream, malt extract, caviar, and many more.
Only those decorated with transfer-printed trade marks
are collected; the unmarked specimens are so common they
are usually left at the dump with unwanted broken glass.

Stoneware whisky bottles with decorative transfer-
printed trade marks are the rarest and most prized in this
category. Very few have yet been found because the vast
majority of dumps in Scotland and Ireland, the traditional
homes of the whisky industry, have still to be excavated.
Proof that they do hold many beautiful stoneware whiskies
is to be seen in the collections of a handful of bottle lovers
who have probed them with digging tools.

NOTES ON RARITY

Australian collectors will benefit most from Britain's
vast resources of stoneware. Many Australians are keen
collectors of stoneware food containers and they should be
able to obtain all the specimens they require from British
diggers. Stoneware whisky fanatics—there are many in

Fig. 22 (*Left*) Early nine-teenth century beer bottle in stoneware

Fig. 23 (*Below*) Transfer-printed caviar pot

Fig. 24 More transfer-printed ginger beers

51

Fig. 25 Miscellaneous ja
from a British dump dat
1895

Australia—will find leaner pickings unless they can encourage more Britons to dig in Scotland and Ireland by
offering some of their sealed case gins as exchanges.

Ginger beer. Transfer-printed or incised. Rating: Very
common. Price guide: 1.
As above; coloured shoulders. Rating: Uncommon.
Price guide: 5.
Miscellaneous pot or jar. Black and white transfer-printed.
Rating: Common. Price guide: 2.
Colour transfer-printed. Rating: Uncommon. Price
guide: 25.
Whisky. Black and white transfer-printed. Rating: Very
rare. Price guide: 60.
Colour transfer-printed. Rating: Extremely rare.
Price guide: 100.

Baby feeders. These bottles were among the first in Britain
to be made in clear glass de-coloured by the addition of
manganese. The commonest shape found is the flattened
oval, but a small number of aqua Hamilton-shaped examples

have turned up in the earliest dumps. Most collectors depend for variety on the amusing trade names usually found on the clear glass specimens. These include Princess, Little Rosebud, Little Pet, Favourite, Cherub, and many more. Double-ended, banana-shaped feeders are not usually collected in Britain as they are regarded as modern bottles.

NOTES ON RARITY

American and Australian collectors who obtain clear glass feeders from Britain will find these bottles turn a deep shade of purple when exposed to strong sunshine for several months.

Flattened oval. Clear glass; internal screw. Rating. Difficult to find. Price guide: 20.
Hamilton shape. Aqua; internal screw. Rating: Rare. Price guide: 60.

Fig. 26   Hamilton-type feeder from a British dump dated 1885

Sauces, pickles, and fruit jars. British dumps are rich in sauce bottles but the majority are unattractive and un-embossed aqua specimens of little interest to collectors. Only those sauce bottles of unusual shape are looked for in dumps and most collectors, following American practice, refer to them as 'peppersauces' even though some have been found with labels indicating they also held vinegar and other varieties of sauce. They are decorated with spirals, rings, or swirls and they vary in height from six to eighteen inches. A very few dark green specimens have come to light but most are aqua. Cathedral-shaped pickle jars in the same shade are also found and collected by a few enthusiasts.

The preserving of fruit and vegetables in air-tight jars was not widely practised in Britain during the nineteenth century as it was in the United States and Australia where fruit jar collecting is now a very popular branch of the hobby. These jars, which have a variety of patented sealing methods, are found in limited numbers in Britain, but most are left at the dump because few collectors in Britain are interested in them.

NOTES ON RARITY

Peppersauce. Aqua; applied lip; spirals, rings, or swirls. Rating: Fairly common. Price guide: 5.
As above; dark green. Rating: Difficult to find. Price guide: 15.
Pickle jar. Aqua; applied lip; cathedral type. Rating: Fairly common. Price guide: 5.
Fruit jar. Aqua or clear glass; internal or external screw. Rating: Uncommon. Price guide: 2.

Miniatures. Miniatures and samples in both glass and stoneware are often found by British dump diggers. These bottles, which were sold or given away by wine merchants, brewers, grocers, and chemists to promote new drinks or products, are enthusiastically collected. Although this method of advertising was not so widely practised in Britain as it was in the United States, there is sufficient variety in shape, size and colour to make miniature collecting an interesting branch of the hobby. Black glass wines and beers are most popular with collectors in this group, followed by miniature transfer-printed ginger beers and sample bottles produced by patent medicine companies.

NOTES ON RARITY

Black glass. 3-4 ins; wine or beer; embossed. Rating: Difficult to find. Price guide: 25.
As above; unembossed. Rating: Fairly common. Price guide: 15.

Stoneware. 2–3 ins; ginger beer; incised or transfer-printed. Rating: Difficult to find. Price guide: 25.

Patent medicine. Up to 4 ins; embossed FREE SAMPLE. Rating: Difficult to find. Price guide: 20.

Pot lids. For the benefit of American readers who may not have seen pot lids let me explain that they are earthenware tops from fish paste, meat paste, toothpaste and cosmetics jars decorated with either black and white or multi-coloured underglaze transfers. There are approximately five hundred known coloured lids and an estimated four thousand black and white specimens. In Britain, Australia, New Zealand and South Africa they are collected with as much enthusiasm as Americans and Canadians show for historical whisky flasks and bitters bottles.

All British diggers excavating dumps dated earlier than 1895 find black and white lids, and those who dig on the earliest dumps around London have turned up some excellent coloured specimens. Most bottle collectors include a few pot lids in their displays, while many of those who specialize in this branch of the hobby can boast of black and white collections totalling several hundred varieties. Their most prized pieces will undoubtedly be those lids used for bears' grease and decorated with pictures of chained or dancing bears. This product was once widely used as a hair dressing and lids from these pots are the most sought-after of all black and white lids. Almost equally prized are those toothpaste, fish paste and meat paste lids with pictorial transfers.

NOTES ON RARITY

A comprehensive black and white pot lid price guide is given in my book, *Collecting Pot Lids* (Pitman, London). Australian and New Zealand collectors will find Britons eager to exchange lids with overseas pot lid enthusiasts

Fig. 27 Bears grease pot l[...]

Fig. 28 (*Below*) Toothpast[...] cold cream and shavin[...] cream pot lids from a Britis[...] dump dated 1880

who have examples of local lids to trade.

Black and white lid. Words only in transfer. Rating: Fairly common. Price guide: 10.
Pictorial transfer: Rating: Difficult to find. Price guide: 30+.
Coloured lid. Pictorial transfer. Rating: Rare. Price guide: 30+.

Clay tobacco pipes. Although clay tobacco pipes are found in nineteenth century refuse dumps throughout the world, it is only in Britain that large numbers of pipes with bowls in the shape of human or animal heads are dug up. (I have no doubt that such pipes will also be found in large numbers in France and Holland when the hobby reaches those countries.) Queen Victoria's crowned head was undoubtedly the most popular subject with pipe makers in nineteenth century Britain, but many other heads, including those of politicians, music-hall artistes and generals were also widely used to decorate pipes. Masonic emblems, the badges of famous regiments, and many intricate abstract patterns are also included in the numerous designs found on tobacco pipes by British diggers.

NOTES ON RARITY

Pipe collecting is almost as popular as pot lid collecting in Britain; some specialists have over two thousand different bowls in their displays. Overseas collectors interested in obtaining specimens will find these items much less expensive than pot lids.

Head bowl. Bowl less than two inches in length. Rating: Fairly common. Price guide: 10.

Bowl over two inches in length. Rating: Difficult to find. Price guide: 20.

Decorated bowl. Bowl less than two inches in length. Rating: Common. Price guide: 5.

Bowl over two inches in length. Rating: Difficult to find. Price guide: 10.

Modern bottles and reproductions. The collecting of twentieth century bottles including Avons and modern whisky figurals is almost unheard of in Britain. The vast majority of collectors regard as valueless any bottle having mould seams passing through its lip and indicating it was probably made after 1900.

At the present time there are no British-made reproduction glass bottles on sale in Britain. One or two Indian and Japanese reproductions of globe-stoppered bottles have been seen in British antique shops in recent years, but these have all been speedily identified by the British Bottle Collectors Club as obvious fakes and details circulated to members. The B.B.C.C. has also made arrangements with the club's sponsor, United Glass, to have dating tests carried out on any bottle suspected by club officials of being a modern reproduction. It is hoped these measures will prevent the growth in Britain of firms reproducing nineteenth century bottles and selling them as antiques.

Restored and repaired bottles. The practice of improving the appearance of bottles recovered from dumps and found to be in less than perfect condition is frowned upon in Britain. The use of oil to hide glass sickness and of plastic resins to repair chips and cracks are regarded as unacceptable practices by the British Bottle Collectors Club. Any bottle so treated would certainly be disqualified from entry in the club's 'Bottle-of-the-Year' competition and it is most unlikely that a British collector would knowingly acquire such a bottle for his collection.

Glass sickness, iridescence, and opalescence. The majority of bottle dumps in Britain are situated in former marshland areas. Such damp conditions produce a mild sickness on about fifty per cent of recovered bottles which clouds the glass but which does not leave the sort of surface encrustations commonly found on bottles dug from dumps in hot, dry regions of the world. These sick bottles are not collected unless they happen to be extremely rare specimens.

The term 'iridescent' is used by British collectors to describe bottles exhibiting a rainbow effect of changing colours on a glass surface free of encrustations. 'Opalesced' bottles exhibit the same play of beautiful colours but they also have white mother-of-pearl encrustations on their surfaces. When iridescence or opalescence cover the entire surface of a bottle they considerably increase the bottle's value.

Pontil marks. British collectors use the terms 'solid pontil' and 'ring-shaped pontil' to describe the marks left by solid iron bar pontil rods and blowpipe pontil rods on the bases of bottles which were attached to these tools before their necks were finished. The term 'nipple pontil' is also widely used in Britain to describe the round, nipple-like mark found on *some* bottles finished with the aid of a bare iron pontil, and also on *many* British bottles finished with the aid of snap-clamp holding devices with cups which often left this type of mark on the base of a bottle. Many collectors who specialize in empontilled bottles do not accept this third term; they confine their collecting to bottles bearing solid and ring-shaped pontil scars.

Books, magazines, clubs, and bottle dealers:
Books:
Sealed bottles, S. Ruggles-Brise, Country Life, London, 1949.

Bottle Collecting, E. Fletcher, Blandford Press, London, 1972.

Treasure Hunting For All, E. Fletcher, Blandford Press, London, 1973.

Digging Up Antiques, E. Fletcher, Pitman, London, 1975.

Treasure Hunters' Guide, E. Fletcher, Blandford Press, London, 1975.

Collecting Pot Lids, E. Fletcher, Pitman, London, 1975.

Magazines:

Bottles and Relics News, Greenacres, Church Road, Black Notley, Braintree, Essex.

Clubs:

British Bottle Collectors Club, National Headquarters, 19 Hambro Avenue, Rayleigh, Essex.

Bottle dealers:

Collectors' Old Bottle Room, 184 Main Road, Biggin Hill, Kent.

The Old Bottle Cellar, 71 Caledonian Road, London, N.1.

International Bottle Trader, 104 Harwal Road, Redcar, Cleveland.

Tony Reynolds' Bottle Shop, 139 Witton Street, Northwich, Cheshire.

Kollectarama Bottle Mart, 39 Vicarage Farm Road, Wellingborough, Northants.

Note: Many more books and magazines devoted to bottle collecting are likely to be published in Britain as the hobby grows in popularity. Overseas readers who wish to be kept informed about future British publications should write, enclosing international reply coupons, to the author whose address is: Edward Fletcher, 104 Harwal Road, Redcar, Cleveland, England.

During the present decade white Australians have become widely interested in their country's brief recorded history. One of the forms this fascination with their past has taken is the collecting of 'Australiana'—that is antiques and other relics of Australia's eighteenth and nineteenth century history. Antique shops are booming; historical societies spring up almost daily; anything which can be positively identified as Australiana is being collected, catalogued, and lovingly preserved. Fortunately bottles have not been missed in the Australiana boom. Indeed, there are probably more bottle collectors in the country than there are collectors of what used to be called Victoriana in the days before the new spirit of individuality swept the land.

The hobby seems to have first taken root in Western Australia in 1970 when the number of Americans living and working in that state began to grow rapidly. Many of these exiled 'Yankees', seeing abandoned farmsteads, derelict gold mining camps, and other surface signs which, back home, usually indicate the presence of 'glass gold' beneath the ground, decided to dig a few speculative holes. They found bottles and within a couple of months many indigenous Western Australians had joined them in the hunt. A number of these early bottle hunters were enthusiastic rockhounds. Their gem-hunting expeditions had already acquainted them with the sites of many old mining settlements in the west and it was on these locations that they concentrated their searches for bottles.

Meanwhile, nearly three thousand miles away on the other side of Australia, a handful of enthusiasts who had made contact with pioneer bottle collectors in Britain were probing dumps around the former goldmining towns of New South Wales and Victoria. Soon there were bottle diggers in every state and local clubs were being formed wherever a handful of enthusiasts banded together. Because of the vast distances which separated many of these small groups they often worked in isolation, quite unaware that

2

The Australian Scene

other enthusiasts thousands of miles away were experiencing similar thrills as they dug into long-forgotten refuse sites.

In addition to their rapidly growing interest in old bottles, a large proportion of these pioneers shared a common interest in rockhounding and amateur lapidary. That hobby was already well established in Australia and it was through correspondence in the form of readers' letters in lapidary magazines that initial contact between many small groups was made. In less than a year each state had its own club and Australia's bottle magazine, *Bottle Collectors Review* was circulating nationally.

The early 1970's were years during which United States influence was strong in Australia. It was a period during which many American hobbies, sports, and pastimes crossed the Pacific and took root 'Down Under'. Hot-rods, surfing, free-fall parachuting, and numerous other American outdoor activities were soon as popular around Sydney as they were around San Francisco. To cater for Australian interest in these activities many American hobbies magazines were soon available on Australian news-stands—and at least two of those magazines carried regular features and articles on the American bottle collecting scene. Through the magazines contact was made with clubs and collectors in the United States and it was from those contacts, and from the American bottle collectors living in Australia, that bottle shows, swap meetings, and other typically American bottle collecting activities were adopted.

In many ways Australian bottle fans enjoy the best of both the old and the new worlds. Seventy-five per cent of the bottles they dig up are of British or Dutch manufacture and they include some of the very best bottles made in those two countries. Of the remaining twenty five per cent about half are rare American specimens made between 1850 and 1880. In addition to this excellent range of bottles Australian collectors can also enjoy a full calendar of events, competitions, exhibitions and other social events comparable with anything available in the United States.

Although American diggers would probably feel quite at home digging Australian dumps, Britons would find conditions totally different to anything experienced in England. There are no large urban dumps; the few that once existed on the outskirts of Sydney, Melbourne and other coastal cities were long ago converted to parks, football grounds, and flower gardens. Digging is almost exclusively confined to abandoned sites—goldmining towns, farmsteads, old logging camps, and derelict country houses. Often a dump will consist of nothing more than a single household's refuse deposited in a small hole at the rear of the house during a period of five to ten years at some time during the nineteenth century. When a dump holds the refuse of more than a dozen households Australians consider it to be a fair-sized site; if fifty households deposited their rubbish on the spot the site is considered to be very large indeed. Compare this with a dump flanking London's riverside which probably contains the refuse from ten thousand Victorian homes!

Digging conditions would also amaze most Britons. The heat in summertime is almost unbearable even though work with the digging tools is made lighter by the fact that most dumps are located in easily-dug sandy soil. Vicious mosquitoes form a constant cloud above diggers' heads and bite sadistically on any exposed flesh; for this reason alone it is far less uncomfortable to sweat out the heat beneath a woollen shirt.

All dumps are populated by an assortment of Australian reptiles and insects. These include tiapan and tiger snakes, death adders, black widow spiders and numerous lizards. Although I did not find a dump which contained all of these creatures living together, I became quite accustomed to watching Australian diggers casually shaking sleeping snakes out of bottles and flicking enormous spiders off their clothing with an air of nonchalance. As an Englishman reared in a land where man is the only creature that can kill, I formed the opinion during my Australian trip that any bottle dug from an Australian dump ought to double in price when sold to provide the digger with adequate danger money!

Finding bottle dumps is not difficult in Australia even though there are no research sources comparable to British council records, and in spite of the fact that many parts of the continent have not been mapped in such detail as the British Ordnance Survey. All you need is a four-wheel-drive vehicle and sufficient experience of wild country to be able to live with its dangers. Suitably equipped and carrying adequate amounts of water if venturing into desert country you simply take to the outback roads and look for derelict buildings and other signs of former human habitation. The best locations are undoubtedly those where large-scale alluvial goldmining was carried out between 1850 and 1890. Many of these gold-rush 'towns' consisted of little more than thousands of tents, but in most of them wooden buildings were erected by store and hotel-keepers. Other visual indications of these vanished communities include derelict gold recovery equipment and mounds of spoil left by the diggers. Another excellent source of information on the locations of worked-out mines are the maps published in Australian rockhounding books and magazines.

Second only to old gold towns as bottle hunting locations are abandoned farms. There are thousands of these small sites situated in areas of unpredictable annual rainfall. Their crumbling barns and fallen fences litter the semi-desert areas where, at some time in the past, men were tricked by a season of good rains into believing they could grow crops. Many bought their farms from city rogues who waited for rainfall before inviting prospective buyers to inspect the properties. The purchasers—most came from Britain in the 1870's—usually managed to scrape a living for a few years, but eventually they were forced to abandon. Fortunately for today's diggers they left a rich, unharvested crop of bottles in their back-gardens.

The recovery of bottles from rivers, harbours and wreck sites by skin-divers is also carried on in Australia. Although this method of collecting is practised by only a small number of enthusiasts the bottles recovered include some of the earliest and most valuable yet found. Other sites which often hold rare whiskies, gins, and cures are worked-out logging camps in forest country.

Imitating American practice, most Australians become specialist collectors almost as soon as they take up the hobby. The branches in which they specialize are dictated as much by the categories in which bottles can be entered at bottle show competitions as by their personal preferences as bottle lovers. They see little value in a good, all-round collection because there is no 'all-round' category in which to enter it in competition. The aim of everyone is to win the top award in a particular category and to this end their collecting is exclusively directed. This attitude accounts for the large volume of trading in bottles that goes on through-out the country; what is valueless to one collector might be priceless to another if it helps him improve his display in the category to which he is dedicated.

At the present time each Australian state has slightly different rules about categories, but efforts are being made to introduce national rules so that collectors from one state visiting a bottle show in another state can compete on equal terms for the coveted awards. Although final decisions have yet to be made it is likely the national categories will be: mineral water patents; case gins, Schnapps, and bitters; patent medicines; glass and stoneware whiskies; inks; household bottles and jars; Avons and other modern bottles; pot lids; black glass; beers, wines, liqueurs and cordials.

For the benefit of British readers I must explain that monetary prizes are either small or non-existent at bottle shows. The 'prize' in each category is a blue ribbon (occasionally a card) embroidered or printed with the competition date and category of bottles. At some of the more important state and national shows winners might also receive inexpensive cups, shields, or medallions which are proudly displayed—with the bottles—in the collector's home. Judging is done on a 100 points system—25 for display, 25 for condition; 25 for rarity, and 25 for variety within the chosen category.

Bottles found

Before considering in detail the various bottles found in Australia's nineteenth century dumps let me explain why so many of them are of British, Dutch, and American origins. Although various attempts were made from 1813 onwards to establish glass bottle factories in Australia it was not until 1872 that this was successfully accomplished by two druggists named Felton and Grimwade who built a factory at Melbourne in that year. The majority of the bottles they produced were for use by their own drug company and it was not until 1890 that the factory was able to supply other Australian bottle users with substantial amounts of its production. In that year the premises were expanded and a number of additional glassblowers recruited from Europe. Following this expansion the firm became known as the Melbourne Glass Bottle Works Company and production increased steadily from that date. Nevertheless, even as late as 1925 Australia was still importing large numbers of empty glass bottles.

Stoneware bottles were more readily available. A successful pottery was established in Sydney in 1803; but it was not until the 1890's that the country became self-sufficient in stoneware pots, jars and bottles.

Throughout the greater part of the nineteenth century British colonial policy was aimed at keeping her various possessions throughout the world completely dependent on the mother country for all manufactured goods while extracting the maximum of raw materials at the lowest possible price from the colonists in order to keep Britain's factories competitive in Europe. Some idea of Australia's dependence on Britain for most of her needs can be grasped from the following list of imported goods offered for sale by one Sydney merchant in 1837:

Newly landed from London and on sale at the warehouse of Charles Beilby: sugar; loaf sugar; hyson skin tea in chests; souchong tea in caddies; shingle nails; batten nails; spike nails; horse nails; flooring brads; clasp nails; tacks; port wine in bottle; port wine in hogsheads; sherry wine in casks; seine twine; tarpaulins; rope; wool bagging; wool packs; gingham; duck frocks; trousers; half hose; regatta shirts; boots and shoes; raisins; oats; rice; soap; flour; mould candles; candlewick; turpentine; paint; white lead; foolscap; paste; wrapping paper; office ink; ink powder; pens and quills; wafers; sealing wax; bottle wax; muskets; fowling pieces; tomahawks; ginger; vinegar; epsom salts; corks; eau de cologne; black lead; thermometers; iron rim locks; brass door locks; drawback locks; shovels; spades; Irish shovels; pit and cross-cut saws; long handled frying pans; iron pots; pickaxes; horse shoes; sickles; sheep shears; flat irons; saw files; floor cloth; bullock chains; salt beef; tierce; pitch; glass of all sizes; blankets; lamps; grass and garden seeds. Terms: under £30—cash; over £30 endorsed bills at 3 months.

Australia's nineteenth century newspapers carry numerous advertisements like this which provide ample evidence of the country's near-total dependence on Britain for supplies of bottled beers, wines, spirits, soft drinks, medicines, foodstuffs, clay tobacco pipes, potted meats, fish pastes—in fact almost everything packaged in the containers excavated by present-day dump diggers.

Holland might have beaten Britain in the race to colonize Australia. Her seamen made the first landfalls on the continent's western coast and Abel Tasman was most unlucky not to have discovered the more hospitable eastern shores in 1642 as Cook did one hundred and twenty eight years later. The Dutch East India Company, which financed many voyages of discovery in the seventeenth century, was firmly established in what is now Indonesia when Tasman set sail from Java on his epic voyage which resulted in the discovery of Tasmania and New Zealand. Had it not been for his unfavourable reports on these new lands the Dutch would certainly have settled them long before the British established themselves. When the first colonists from England did arrive it was not long before the Dutch East India Company began trading with them.

The English who came to Australia retained their taste for Dutch gin, a commodity the Dutch East India Company was happy to supply. Most of it arrived in beautiful shoulder-sealed free-blown case bottles, but marine arachaeological evidence gathered by divers working on seventeenth and eighteenth century Dutch wrecks off Australia's western coast indicates that in those days gin was also shipped in stoneware Bellarmine jugs. In later years, when merchants in Sydney, Melbourne and other cities were importing Dutch gin direct from Holland, the case bottles in which it came were almost all mould-blown. They did, however, retain their applied shoulder seals and it is these bottles which present-day diggers find in large numbers in Australian dumps.

The discovery of gold in New South Wales and Victoria in the 1850's brought thousands of gold-fevered men from California to Australia. Many of them, including the two who made the first strikes in both states, were in fact Australians who had learned the skills of recovering alluvial gold in the Californian '49 rush. These men and the hoards of ex-Californian Americans, Germans, Frenchmen and Irishmen who came with them brought, in addition·to their gold fever, an unquenchable thirst for American whisky, bitters, and quack medicines. Local merchants and store-keepers were soon obliging them with ample supplies shipped from San Francisco and other American ports. The following advertisements are typical of many which appeared in Australian newspapers between 1851 and 1880:

Hotalong Old Bourbon Whisky is gradually winning its way into popularity. Everyone drinks it in America, and Australians who visit the Great Republic almost immediately contract a fondness for it. Sole agent: Barron, Moxham & Co., Sydney.

Now landing: 250 cases of Stoughton Bitters; 150 cases of Lediards' Knickerbocker Schnapps, the great American beverage; 50 cases of American Cocktail Bitters; 50 cases of Lediards' Stomach Bitters; 50 cases of Stoughton's Elixir; 11 cases of American painkiller; 43 cases of American patent medicines. Also Short Horn American Bourbon Whisky for consumptives and invalids. Less heating than brandy or Irish and Scotch whiskies. Importer: S. Hoffnung & Co., Sydney.

The rush to the diggings! Diggers can be supplied with the proper and most useful American medicines for the new diggings at Watson's Drug Store, Sydney.

Thousands of these American bottles found their way into rubbish dumps around the goldfields of Ophir, the Turon, Ballarat, Bendigo, Mount Alexander, and wherever the gleam of yellow metal beckoned former Californians who brought their drinking habits with them. Together with the many rarities from Britain and Holland these bottles make up the fascinating assortment found by Australian diggers and briefly described in the remainder of this chapter.

Mineral water patents. You will have to look very hard indeed even in Britain, home of internally-stoppered mineral water bottles, to find collections equal to some of those owned by Australian mineral water patents enthusiasts. The reason for this is not that Australians are digging earlier dumps; it is because considerably more varieties of Britain's *unusual* patent mineral water bottles were sold in Australia than were sold in the southeast of England between 1870 and 1890.

Even before 1870 the consumption of aerated waters in

Australia, with its warm, thirst-inducing climate, was greater per head of population than it was in Britain. At the very beginning of Victoria's reign sales of these beverages were brisk in New South Wales as is shown by the following advertisements from newspapers of the day:

For Sale: A soda water machine with 30 gross of soda water bottles and 200 gross of corks. Apply W. James, King St., Sydney. [1837].

J. Bossley (Late A. Foss) is pleased to announce that he can supply bottled soda water at The Fountain, Pitt St., Sydney. Also those refreshing and agreeable aerated beverages ginger, lemonade, magnesia, and Seidlitz water. N.B. No connection with any other house in Sydney. [1837].

Smith's superior soda water and lemonade. J. Smith begs to inform the persons whom he has refused to supply, and the public generally, that he has received, ex-TROPIC, a large quantity of soda water bottles, so that he will now be able to supply them with any quantity, either town or country, and by strict attention to business, bottling, and also supplying his customers himself, hopes a continuance of that liberal support which he has received during the time he has been in business at 45 Upper Pitt St., Sydney. [1842].

No doubt all of the above firms and their competitors were bottling their aerated waters in pointed-bottomed, aqua Hamiltons, as were all British makers at the time. The situation remained unchanged until the 1870's when many Australian wholesale merchants began to import the newfangled internally-stoppered bottles that had already become popular in Britain. In 1879 Mason Bros, a Sydney wholesale company, advertised, 'Lamont patent stoppered mineral water bottles and others for sale'. Prosser & Co, wholesale druggists of the same city, advertised, 'Patent and plain soda water bottles and stoneware ginger beer bottles' in the same year, as did many other importers as consumption of bottled soft drinks continued to increase.

A number of British mineral water makers, attracted by the growing market, were also shipping British-made and bottled beverages to the colony at this time. Schweppe & Co of London advertised widely that their 'soda water, lemonade, Malvern water, potash water, and quinine tonic water' were 'available from all chemists and wine merchants throughout the colony.' The Apollinaris Company announced that their 'Apollinaris water, the Queen of table waters,' was 'available in stoneware bottles and soda water bottles branded "Apollinaris Brunner" around an anchor, from all winemerchants and grocers.' Ross & Co of Belfast reminded customers that their agent, Washington H. Soul of Sydney, had ample supplies of their 'ginger-ale, lemonade, and limejuice'.

This market for British-made drinks dwindled rapidly after 1880 when Australian manufacturers began to import the most up-to-date British machinery for their expanding factories. They stressed in the advertisements that their products were much fresher than imported brands and often claimed superiority in flavour and other qualities, Thus, Dalm & Oertel, of The Mineral Water Works, Sydney, were pleased to advertise, in 1883, that they could supply 'freshly made and bottled seltzer, soda water, ginger ale, tonic, Friedrickshaller bitter water, potash water, and Baden-Baden water of quality unequalled by imported brands.'

It was these go-ahead colonial companies which provided markets for British bottlemakers including Rylands, Lamont, Lumb, Turner, Kilner, Barrett & Elers, Breffit, Riley, and others who shipped large quantities of blue and dark green Hamiltons; blue, amber, and red-lipped Codd Originals, Acmes, Reliances, and Empresses; Crystal Valves; and even larger quantities of aqua Hamiltons and copies of Codd's and Rylands' expired patents.

Some Australian bottle historians writing on the subject of patent-stoppered bottles found in Australia in the early days of the hobby's growth mistakenly took the names of one or two British glass bottle makers—usually found embossed on the bases or lower bodies of mineral water bottles—to be the names of patent stopper inventors. Thus they occasionally refer to 'Turner' or 'Dewsbury' patents when describing Rylands' or Codd's expired patents made in the 1880's (and later) by Turner & Co, bottle-makers, of Dewsbury, Yorkshire. Similar bottles made by the Kilner Glassworks have also been wrongly indentified as special patents.

There are two mineral water bottles found in large numbers in Australian dumps which will be of particular interest to British collectors because it is possible these were locally invented and not copied or made under licence from British inventors. If this is the case early examples would, of course, have been made in Britain for their inventors because there were no glassworks in Australia which could have manufactured them. The first is the so-called 'Maugham's Patent' which a Briton might describe as an extra-long improved Hamilton. It might in fact be nothing more than that; none have been found with internal stoppers still inside and most Australians consider the bottle to have been cork-sealed. On the other hand, the internal shoulders of these bottles are con-stricted and suggest an internal rubber-ball stopper might have been used. The name 'Maugham's Patent' has been given to this bottle because a number have been found bearing embossing which reads, 'Maugham's Patent Carrara Water'—a reference to the contents and *not* to the bottle.

The second bottle is the 'Gledhill Patent'. In shape it is not unlike the American 'Hutchinson Patent' or a British black glass dumpy ginger beer. Examples have been found with internal stoppers in them and these have proved to be soft rubber balls which were obviously held against the internal shoulders of the bottle by gas pressure. Research at the Patent Office in London confirms that the patent specifications for this bottle were submitted on 24 February 1874 by E. Hunt on behalf of G. Gledhill. Mr. Gledhill's nationality is not given, but as these bottles are found only in Australia and New Zealand there seems little doubt about their origins.

Because of the very dry conditions found in Australian dumps many bottles with 'Lightning' stoppers survive complete with their wire bales. Other finds include a few black glass Barrett's internal screw stoppers and a fair number of American 'Hutchinson Patents'.

Fig. 29 Cobalt blue Hamilton found in Australia

NOTES ON RARITY

Rylands' Valve; on Reliance and Acme. Rating: Rare. Price guide: 100.

Rylands' coloured lips; on Original, Bulb, Empress, Acme, and Reliance. Rating: Uncommon. Price guide: 60.

on Valve. Rating: Very rare. Price guide: 150.

on Codd-Hamilton hybrids. Rating: Rare. Price guide: 100.

Coloured Codd's Original (and other one-way pourers); dark green. Rating: Uncommon. Price guide: 40.

brown. Rating: Uncommon. Price guide: 60.

blue. Rating: Rare. Price guide: 100.

Coloured Hamiltons: As above.

Lamont's Patents: Rating: Fairly common. Price guide: 30.

Maugham's Patent: Rating: Common. Price guide: 15.

Gledhill's Patent: Rating: Common. Price guide: 15.

Barrett and Elers' Wooden Plug: Rating: Rare. Price guide: 100.

Codd's Original; aqua. Rating: Common. Price guide: 5.

Other internally stoppered bottles in aqua: Rating: Common. Price guide: 10+.

Hamiltons in aqua: Rating: Common. Price guide: 5.

Stoneware ginger beers; incised or transfer printed. Rating: common. Price guide: 1.

Fig. 30 Red-lipped Codd from Victoria

73

Fig. 31 (*Left*) Internal
stoppered bottles fr
Tasmania

Fig. 32 (*Below left*) Coc
Hamilton hybrids dug fr
a dump in New Sou
Wales. The specimen
extreme right is pale bl
in colour

Fig. 33 (*Below*) Deep cob
blue Codd from Austral

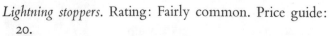

Lightning stoppers. Rating: Fairly common. Price guide:
20.

Barrett's internal screw. Rating: Uncommon. Price guide:
40.

Hutchinson stoppers. Rating: Fairly common. Price guide:
20.

Inks. Inks found in Australian dumps are almost all of British manufacture. The commoner aqua, and occasionally dark green and blue varieties—eight-siders, boats (called 'ships' or 'cabins' by Australians), rounds, ribbed squares, ribbed oblongs, and bells—differ from British finds only in that they are much more often embossed with the names of ink makers. I suspect embossing was used in preference (or in addition) to paper labels on many British ink bottles bound for overseas markets as a precaution against labels falling off if cargoes became wet during long sea voyages.

Few British ink makers seem to have used shapes such as cones, umbrellas, three-sides, teakettles, and igloos for Australian markets and these bottles are even rarer in Australia than they are in Britain. At the time of writing no cottage inks have been recovered from Australian dumps. Stoneware inks, particularly bulk inks with capacities of one pint or more, are much less common than in Britain.

NOTES ON RARITY

Eight-sided; aqua; sheared lip. Rating: Common. Price guide: 1.

Boat; aqua; sheared lip. Rating: Common. Price guide: 1.

Round; aqua; machine-made. Rating: Common. Price guide: 3.

Ribbed square; aqua; sheared lip. Rating: Common. Price guide: 3.

Ribbed oblong; aqua; sheared lip. Rating: Common. Price guide: 3.

Bell; aqua; sheared lip. Rating: Less common. Price guide: 5.

Coloured specimens of any of above:
  Dark green. Rating: Very uncommon. Price guide: 15.
  Light blue. Rating: Uncommon. Price guide: 12.
  Cobalt blue. Rating: Uncommon. Price guide: 10.

Note: For embossed specimens of any of above inks

Price Guide should be doubled.

Cone, umbrella, barrel, three-sider, igloo, teakettle; any colour; any lip. Rating: Very rare. Price guide: 100+.

Cottage; any colour; any lip. Rating (British and American specimens in Australian collections): Exceedingly

rare. Price guide: 200 +.

Round, stoneware. Rating: Uncommon. Price guide: 5.

Bulk; stoneware; one pint or more. Rating: Uncommon. Price guide: 10.

Bitters. Australia's goldfield dumps have proved rich in bitters bottles. Finds include Drake's Plantation Bitters in honey amber, Soule's Hop Bitters in amber and black glass, Hartwig Kantorowicz in milk glass, Philadelphia Hop Bitters (many specimens have reversed ‘embossing), New York Hop Bitters in two sizes, Frisco Hop Bitters, Gipsland Hop Bitters, Dr. Bell's Kidney and Liver Bitters, Queensland Hop Bitters, Rowlands' Hop Bitters, Van Bergh's Hop Bitters, Royal Kent Hop Bitters, Warner's Safe Bitters, Utica Bitters, Iron Bitters, and large numbers of the commoner German Bitterquell bottle, the well-known Hostetter's specimen, and Siegert's Angostura Bitters.

Evidence from nineteenth century newspaper advertisements suggests that, as in Britain, a number of varieties still await discovery in Australia. These include, in addition to those mentioned in the British chapter of this book, African Stomach Bitters, Atwood's Bitters, Boston Malt Bitters and California Fig and Herb Bitters. There may be others which were not so widely advertised.

It is interesting to note that although the well-known American Dr. Doyle's Hop Bitters bottle appears absent from Australia, as it is from Britain, Australians find both amber *and* black glass specimens of the very similar Dr Soule's Hop Bitters bottle. This suggests supplies of that particular brew reached Australia from both the United States and Britain.

NOTES ON RARITY

Many Australians are keen bitters collectors and this is reflected in prices which are generally high for all but the most common bitters bottles.

Drake's Plantation Bitters. Rating: Rare. Price guide: 80.

Siegert's Angostura Bitters. Rating: Common. Price guide: 10.

Dr. Soule's Hop Bitters; amber and black. Rating: Rare. Price guide: 70.

Hartwig Kantorowicz; milk glass. Rating: Uncommon. Price guide: 40.

Bitterquell. Rating: Common. Price guide: 5.

Dr. Bell's Kidney and Liver Bitters. Rating: Uncommon. Price guide: 30.

Philadelphia Hop Bitters. Rating: Rare. Price guide: 70.
—reversed embossing. Rating: Rarer. Price guide: 100.

New York Hop Bitters; both sizes. Rating; Uncommon. Price guide: 40.

Frisco Hop Bitters. Rating: Uncommon. Price guide: 40.

Gipsland Hop Bitters. Rating: Uncommon. Price guide: 40.

Queensland Hop Bitters. Rating: Rare. Price guide: 70.

Rowlands' Hop Bitters. Rating: Rare. Price guide: 70.

Van Bergh's Hop Bitters. Rating: Rare. Price guide: 70.

Royal Kent Hop Bitters. Rating: Rare. Price guide: 80.

Warner's Safe Hop Bitters. Rating: Rare. Price guide: 85.

Utica Bitters. Rating: Uncommon. Price guide: 40.

Iron Bitters. Rating: Uncommon. Price guide: 40.

Hostetter's Bitters. Rating: Common. Price guide: 15.

Fig. 35 A European se bottle found in Syd Harbour

Sealed bottles. Apart from sealed case gins (discussed in the next section) Australian dumps contain very few sealed bottles. One of the reasons for this shortage is that prior to the 1850's gold rushes, when sealed wine bottles were in common use in Britain, the population of Australia did not rise above two hundred and fifty thousand. Although substantial quantities of wine were shipped from Britain in those days most of it arrived in barrels to be sold 'on tap' in Australia's pubs and hotels or to be bottled in plain, unembossed and unsealed bottles by local merchants who applied their own paper labels.

True, the discovery of gold produced a population explosion, but the people who came to Australia's shores were not the types to consume large quantities of vintage wine. Their tastes were for gin, whisky and bitters; their arrival did little to increase the numbers of sealed wine bottles finding their way into Australian dumps. Nor did the growth of Australia's own wine-making industry in the mid-Victorian era add to the numbers of sealed wine bottles in circulation. As with most imported wines, the Australian product was either sold in barrels or in unmarked bottles which were made in England and imported by Australian wine merchants. Those drinks sold in sealed bottles in Britain after 1860—cherry liqueur, choice French wines, and more expensive brands of beer—were either too expensive or too little known in Australia to have left

78

more than a handful of 'empties' for today's collectors.

A few extremely rare seventeenth, eighteenth, and early nineteenth century sealed bottles of onion and squat cylindrical shapes have been recovered by divers working on wrecks around Australia's coastline. Archaeological digs on very early Australian settlements have also produced a few of these bottles.

NOTES ON RARITY

Onion shape; black or olive green glass; freeblown; pontil. Rating: Exceedingly rare. Price guide: 200.
Squat cylindrical shape; black or green; freeblown; pontil. Rating: Very rare. Price guide: 180.
Continental wine; turn-mould; aqua or shade of green. Rating: Rare. Price guide: 100.
—black glass. Rating: Rare. Price guide: 150.
British seals, turn-mould or two or three-piece mould; aqua or shade of green. Rating: Very rare. Price guide: 150.
—black glass. Rating: Very rare. Price guide: 160.

Fig. 36 Sealed whisky bottle exported in the late nineteenth century

Case gins and Schnapps. That the early settlers from Britain brought their liking for Dutch gin to the new colonies in Australia and that their tastes were satisfied by merchants of the Dutch East India Company are proved by the large numbers of gin bottles found in Dutch wrecks around Australia's coasts. By the beginning of Victoria's reign Australian merchants were competing with the Dutch East India Company and importing the drink direct from Europe—as is shown by the following contemporary newspaper advertisements:

Newly landed from Greenwich; fine Dutch gin in two gallon case bottles. Betts Bros., Importers, Sydney. [1837].

Solomon Moses, Travellers' Home Inn, Goulburn. Always on hand; extensive stocks of best Geneva. [1837].

79

Best quality Schiedam gin in cases; direct from Amsterdam.
T. W. Campbell, George St., Sydney. [1842].

The earliest bottles were beautifully crude freeblown specimens with rough pontils and large shoulder seals. By 1870 most of them were being made in embossed two or three-piece moulds, but fortunately for today's collectors the practice of applying shoulder seals was continued throughout the nineteenth century. This has left a rich assortment of tapering, olive-green bottles bearing the seals of Dutch distilleries in most of Australia's Victorian dumps. Commonest finds are those bearing seals impressed with the monogram 'AVH'. These bottles were used by A. vanHoboken of Rotterdam. Another fairly common example carries a shoulder seal impressed with an anchor. 'Anchor Brand' gin was sold by J. deKuyper. Rarer seals carry pictures including birds, bears, horses, trees and human figures.

There is one case gin found in Australian dumps which, although it does not carry a shoulder seal, is as prized for its embossing as some of the rarer seals. This is the bottle used for Willem Zoom's Cosmopoliet Gin. One face of the bottle shows an embossed figure of a man holding a glass of gin in his hand.

Straight-sided Schnapps bottles are also found in large numbers in Australian dumps; most collections include more than fifty different specimens. The majority carry only the names of Dutch distilleries, but several have pictorial embossing including castles, animals, and trees.

NOTES ON RARITY

Most Australian collectors have substantial numbers of AVH and ANCHOR sealed case gins available as trade items. In view of the rarity of all sealed case gins in Britain and America it should not be difficult for Australians to obtain good mineral water patents, bitters, and black glass specimens in exchange for them.

Case gin; freeblown; shoulder seal. Rating: Rare. Price guide: 60.

two or three-mould; pictorial seal. Rating: Fairly common. Price guide: 40.

two or three-mould; AVH or ANCHOR seal. Rating: Common. Price Guide: 20.

freeblown or mould-blown; no seal. Rating: Common. Price guide: 10.

two-mould; COSMOPOLIET. Rating: Rare. Price guide: 50.

Schnapps; embossed with distillers' names. Rating: Fairly common. Price guide: 20.

pictorial embossing. Rating: Fairly common. Price guide: 40.

Fig. 37 A free-blown case gin bottle recovered from an early nineteenth century wreck off Australia's northern coast

Black glass. Both dark green and dark brown varieties of 'black' glass are as difficult to find in Australian dumps as they are in Britain and America. Most Scotch and Irish whisky distillers who shipped spirits to Australia in the late nineteenth century used stoneware containers, though a few favoured the same black bottles used for the home markets. When richly embossed these black whiskies are highly prized by Australian collectors.

Black turn-mould wines used by Australian wine producers are of little interest because they lack seals, but some Australian breweries used black bottles up to the 1920's and these containers, when embossed, are enthusiastically collected. Most of them utilized cork stoppers long after the introduction of crown closures in America and Britain. The string or wire securing the cork was fastened to a string-ring below the neck just as it was on eighteenth century beer bottles. Australians refer to bottles using this type of closure as 'ring seals' and there are many collectors who devote their entire displays to Australian ring seal beers in black glass.

Fig. 38 Turn-mould wi
bottles found in Australi

It is worth noting that even though population figures did not reach one million until 1870 the number of embossed beers found in Australia's late nineteenth century dumps almost equals the numbers found in British dumps of similar age. The main reason for this is that after 1880 many Australian breweries (there were seven hundred registered in that year) turned to brewing lager beer in response to popular demand for the brew in preference to traditional English beers and ales. Unlike English beer, lager cannot be stored for long periods in wooden barrels; it must be bottled soon after brewing otherwise it becomes unpalatable. Hence the large numbers of beer bottles used by Australian breweries.

NOTES ON RARITY

Most Australian collectors would be happy to trade some of their sealed case gins or unusual mineral water patents for British and American black glass.

Whisky; pictorial embossing. Rating: Rare. Price guide: 60.

Wine; turn-mould. Rating: Common. Price guide: 5.

Fig. 39 Unusual black glass wine bottle from Australia

Beer; ring seal; pictorial embossing. Rating: Fairly common. Price guide: 20.

Acid etched glass. The use of acid to etch trade marks and brand names on the surfaces of bottles was rarely practised in Australia. A few breweries employed this method of labelling their bottles but acid etching was not used by hotels and public houses as it was in.Britain.

NOTES ON RARITY

Beer; pictorial etching. Rating: Rare. Price guide: 40.

Blue glass: Most blue glass bottles found in Australian dumps are of British origins. Three, six, and eight-sided poisons embossed 'Not to be taken' are less common than in Britain, while castor oils are found in large numbers. Syrups bottles, the wedge-shaped Price's Patent Candle Company's bottle, and the oblong Mexican Hair Renewer are unknown. Rare finds include blue vinegar bottles of intricate ribbed design and blue fluted salad oils in various sizes.

NOTES ON RARITY

Poison; three, six, or eight-sided; embossed NOT TO BE TAKEN. Rating: Uncommon. Price guide: 10.
Castor oil; cylindrical; sheared or applied lip; unembossed. Rating: Common. Price guide: 5.
Vinegar; ribbed; applied lip. Rating: Rare. Price guide: 40.
Salad oil; fluted; applied lip. Rating: Rare. Price guide: 25.

Patent medicines. Bottles used for both American and British patent medicines are found in most Australian dumps, but specimens embossed with the names or trade marks of Australian patent medicine manufacturers are rare in spite of the fact that contemporary newspapers carried many advertisements for Australian-made painkillers, snakebite medicines, cough cures, and similar products. Digging evidence suggests most of these locally màde concoctions were sold in bottles bearing paper labels.

The American 'Doctors' Warner, Radams, Townsend, and Kilmer are all well represented by their empties and obviously enjoyed considerable success in the goldmining areas of the country. Sarsaparilla was a popular remedy for 'blood purification' and Dr. Townsend had a number of rivals whose products also sold well in. Australia. They included Ayer's Sarsaparilla, J. V. Babcode's Gold Medal Sarsaparilla, Denis' Georgia Sarsaparilla, Hair's Sarsaparilla, Buchan's Sarsaparilla, Bristol's Sarsaparilla, Munro's Sarsaparilla, and Dr. Bayley's Celebrated Sarsaparilla.

Rarer British patent medicine bottles such as Turlington's Balsam and Daffy's Elixir have not yet been found by Australian diggers, though large numbers of commoner varieties have turned up.

Fig. 40 Australian Warner's Safe Cure from Melbourne

NOTES ON RARITY

American collectors should note that, as in Britain, many American patent medicine bottles found in Australia differ in both glass colour and embossing from specimens found in the U.S.A.

Commoner British types. Rating: Large numbers found. Price guide: 1–5.

Sarsaparillas. Rating: Much sought after by collectors. Price guide: 40+.

Australian varieties. Rating: Rare. Price guide: 40+.

Warner's Safe Cure, Melbourne; amber-brown; applied lip; approx. 9½ ins. Rating: Scarce. Price guide: 40.

85

as above; approx. $11\frac{1}{2}$ ins. Rating: Scarce. Price guide: 50.

(*Note:* Olive green Warner's Safe Cures are unknown in Australia.)

Radam's Microbe Killer. Rating: Rare. Price guide: 80.

Dr. Kilmer's Swamp Root Kidney Cure. Rating: Scarce. Price guide: 30.

Stoneware. Although a few American stoneware bottles, including bourbon jugs, reached Australia in the nineteenth century most stoneware containers found in Australia are of British origins. More than one thousand different transfer-printed ginger beers have been found by Australian diggers and many of them bear the incised trade marks of British potteries. Blacking pots, bulk inks, and a wide variety of food jars are similarly marked and all are enthusiastically collected by Australians.

Most popular of all stoneware containers are transfer-printed whisky bottles. Some two hundred varieties bearing the ornate trade marks of Scotch and Irish whisky distillers have so far been recovered and the search for new specimens continues. Few British collectors can match the displays exhibited by Australian enthusiasts in spite of the fact that almost all of the exhibits were made in Britain. Some of the most prized specimens have pictorial transfers commemorating notable dates including Queen Victoria's 1897 Jubilee and the Relief of Mafeking. Others are decorated with two and three-coloured transfers.

Fig. 41 Australian gin beer bottle

NOTES ON RARITY

Although quite large numbers of stoneware whisky bottles are found in Australia demand keeps prices high.

Ginger beer; transfer-printed or incised. Rating: Very common. Price guide: 1.

86

Fig. 42 Miscellaneous stone-ware from an Australian dump

as above; coloured shoulders. Rating: Common. Price guide: 3.

Miscellaneous pots and jars; black and white transfer-printed. Rating: Common. Price guide: 10.

colour transfers; Rating: Uncommon. Price guide: 30.

Whisky; black and white transfer-printed. Rating: Uncommon. Price guide: 80.

colour transfers. Rating: Rare. Price guide: 150.

Baby feeders. Australians call them 'nursers' but they differ very little from those found in British dumps. All were exported to the Australian colonies by British wholesale chemists including Maw, Sanger and Mather. As in Britain, the majority are of flattened oval shape. Many Australians also collect the more modern double-ended 'banana' shaped specimens. Hamilton-shaped aqua specimens are unknown.

NOTES ON RARITY

Flattened oval; clear glass; internal screw. Rating: Fairly common. Price guide: 15.

87

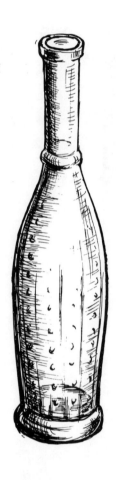
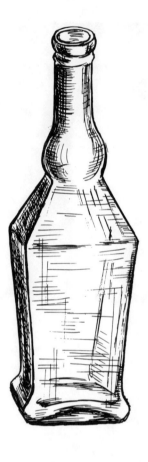

Banana shape; clear glass; double-ended. Rating: Uncommon. Price guide: 10.

Sauces, pickles, and fruit jars. Many of Australia's late nineteenth and early twentieth century sauce manufacturers
used attractive bottles of ribbed and fluted designs for their
products. A few favoured coloured glass but the majority
used clear or aqua bottles which are, nevertheless, considerably more eye-catching than most British sauces.
Salad oil and vinegar bottles are even more attractive, as

Fig. 45 Australian fruit jar

the Australian names for them—'whirlies and dimples'—
suggest. They are found in a wide range of sizes and
designs and, together with pickle jars of equal variety, form
an important branch of bottle collecting in Australia.

Fruit jars are also enthusiastically collected. The numerous
American specimens found in Australian dumps indicate
that fruit and vegetable preserving was as popular in
nineteenth century Australia as it was in the United States.
Mason's jars with porcelain and milk glass closures are
abundant; so too are British-made jars with embossed
trade marks of Australian fruit preserving companies.

Sauce; fluted or ribbed; aqua. Rating: Common. Price guide: 5.

as above; blue or dark green glass. Rating: Uncommon. Price guide: 20.

Salad oil; fluted; aqua. Rating: Common. Price guide: 10.

as above; blue or dark green. Rating: Uncommon. Price guide: 25.

Vinegar; ribbed or dimpled; aqua. Rating: Common. Price guide: 10.

as above; blue or dark green glass. Rating: Uncommon. Price guide: 30.

Fruit jar. Rating: Common. Price guide: 10–25.

Pot lids. Less than fifty black and white lids bearing the names and addresses of Australian chemists have been found in Australian dumps. Almost all of these, were made in Britain for British wholesale chemists who re-sold them to colonial retailers. The transfers were designed in such a way that a blank space was left on each lid into which the name and address of a retailer could be inserted using a lettered transfer. Very few nineteenth century Australian chemists or druggists dealt directly with British potteries when ordering earthenware pots with transfer-printed lids because they were unable to place sufficiently large orders to make the production of individual pots an economic proposition. The few whose businesses were large enough usually engaged local potteries and the quality of the transfers on their lids is much inferior to those found on lids made in the mother country.

Thousands of British lids, including many coloured specimens have been found by Australian diggers who are as enthusiastic about pot lid collecting as are most diggers in Britain. Toothpaste lids used by Britain's largest companies (Gosnell, Woods, Maw, etc.) are fairly common; but lids from British fish and meat paste pots are. difficult to find.

NOTES ON RARITY

British coloured lid collectors should note that although prices for Pratt pot lids are generally higher in Australia than in Britain few Australians distinguish between common and rare lids. All change hands at about the same prices.

Black and white lids; words only on transfer; British lid.
Rating: Fairly common. Price guide: 20.
—words only on transfer; Australian chemist. Rating: Scarce. Price guide: 50.
—pictorial transfer; British lid. Rating: Scarce. Price guide: 60+.
—pictorial transfer; Australian chemist. Rating; Rare. Price guide: 100+.
Coloured lids; pictorial transfer. Rating: Rare. Price guide: 100.

Clay tobacco pipes. Although advertisements in Australia's nineteenth century newspapers reveal that both British and French clay tobacco pipes were imported in the nineteenth century, digging evidence indicates that almost all were undecorated 'cutty' specimens. For this reason there is little interest in pipe collecting in Australia.

Modern bottles and reproductions. The collecting of Avons, modern whisky figurals and modern miniatures are popular branches of bottle collecting in Australia. There is also a growing interest in the collecting of American-made reproductions of nineteenth century bottles, and one or two 'commemoratives' have been specially made in Australia for sale at national bottle shows and other events. Following American practice, Australians adhere rigidly to price guides and 'encyclopaedias' issued by official clubs and U.S. sponsors of this industry.

Fig. 46 Australian pot lid transfers

Restored and repaired bottles. Although much less valued than perfect specimens, repaired bottles are generally acceptable in Australian bottle collecting circles. Many collectors repair lip chips and other imperfections with plastic resins and other materials. Oil is widely used to hide glass sickness and to improve the appearance of bottles displayed in collectors' homes or exhibited at bottle shows.

Fig. 47 Sickness as seen many Australian bottles

Glass sickness, iridescence, and opalescence. The sandy conditions found in many Australian dumps produce severe sickness and surface encrustations on more than seventy-five per cent of recovered bottles. It is this high rate of imperfection in excavated bottles which encourages Australians to use large amounts of oil in attempts to hide it. Many of Australia's iridescent bottles are quite spectacular in their rainbow colours; British bottles displaying this effect would pale to insignificance beside them. White opalescence is much less common. Both effects greatly increase the value of any bottle.

Sun-coloured glass. The purple or amethyst colouring found in manganese de-coloured glass bottles which have been exposed to prolonged sunshine is vividly seen in many Australian specimens. Sauce bottles, pickles and fruit jars are often found in such deep shades of purple they can be mistaken for black glass at first sight. The effect is seen best on bottles that have lain on the surface of the ground for eighty years or more, but such is the intensity of Australian sunshine any excavated bottle made from glass containing manganese can be 'purpled' by placing it in direct sunshine for a single summer. It is is a common sight to see rows of bottles laid out on garage roofs around bottle collectors' homes to receive the required amount of ultra-violet light.

Sun-starved British collectors should note that there are thousands of British bottles that were made between 1880 and 1914 which contain large amounts of manganese. All would turn various shades of purple if shipped to Australia for a few months. Shipping costs are high, but the expense could be justified if the right bottles were chosen. These include *clear glass* Codds, coffin flasks, pumpkin seeds, and inks. All of these would be highly valued in Britain after exposure to Australian sunshine.

Pontil marks. Australian collectors use American terms to describe pontil scars. These are explained in the next chapter.

Books, magazines, clubs, and bottle dealers.

Books:
Bottles in Australian collections, James Lerk, Cambridge Press, Bendigo, Victoria, 1972.

Magazines:

Australian Bottle Collectors Review, P.O. Box 245, Deniliquin, N.S.W., 2710.

Clubs:

There are five state clubs and dozens of local clubs. Up-to-date information on addresses, etc. can be obtained by writing to T. Bannon, Secretary, Australian Bottle Collectors Association, 10 Patching Avenue, Noble Park, Victoria, 3174.

Bottle dealers:

Mayama Antique Bottles, 38 Drake Street, Osborne Park, W.A. 6017.
Brian Murray, 4–3a Powell Street, Coogee, N.S.W. 2034.

The New Zealand Scene

Bottle collectors in New Zealand find very similar bottles to those dug up by their Australian cousins. There are, however, no American bottles in New Zealand's nineteenth century dumps, most of which are located in former goldmining areas or near abandoned sawmills in timber country. The lack of American bottles in these sites is more than made up for by the large numbers of British-made, transfer-printed stoneware whiskies, Dutch case gins, and beautiful salad oils and vinegars recovered by diggers.

At the present time there are no bottle collectors' clubs in the country. Enthusiasts meet occasionally in each others homes to exchange finds and to talk shop, and most of them subscribe to the *Australian Bottle Collectors Review* which publishes articles and letters from readers in New Zealand.

The notes on rarity and the price guides quoted in the foregoing Australian section apply equally to New Zealand.

On 15 October 1959 at Sacramento, California, a small group of relic hunters, divers, and amateur treasure hunters formed the world's first bottle collectors' club—The Antique Bottle Collectors Association of California. Initial membership totalled less than one hundred, but from this inconspicuous beginning was born a hobby which, within ten years, was to rival coin and stamp collecting in popularity and which, by 1974, had a following in the United States totalling more than one million enthusiasts.

Many of the Californians who helped form the first club were already experienced relic hunters. Some owned metal detectors and spent their weekends seeking lost or hidden valuables and relics around California's ghost towns. A lucky few found hoards of gold and silver, but the majority had to be content with old guns, mining tools, and other items of 'Americana' recovered from these sites. All were fascinated by the bottles they found in abundance and they coined the term 'glass gold' to describe bitters, whiskies, and patent medicine bottles dug from mining town dumps. It was a fortunate coincidence that these first sites excavated in the United States contained sufficient varieties of unusual and beautiful bottles to spark interest in collecting them at a time when they were valueless as antiques. Had the dumps contained only common beers and soda water bottles it is unlikely the hobby would have attracted great interest until many years later. Fortunately those old 'forty-niners' preferred stronger medicine!

As a hobby 'ghost towning' was confined to the western states where metals including gold, silver and copper had been extensively mined in the nineteenth century. The new hobby—bottle collecting—was soon found to be equally productive in other states. It could be profitably pursued wherever nineteenth century refuse had been dumped—on ranches and old homesteads in the mid-Western states; around logging towns in Washington's timber country; on old plantations in the deep South; in the mangrove swamps of Florida; and on the outskirts of big cities in the

East. Within two or three years every state in the Union could boast at least one bottle collectors' club, and in many states dozens of small-town clubs were also formed by enthusiasts who shared a common interest in local bottles. With characteristic American flair for organisation, promotion and publicity the founders of these clubs were soon arranging shows, meetings and competitions aimed at bringing the activities of their particular group to the attention of fellow Americans. The larger clubs began to produce regular newsletters and it was not long before enterprising publishers issued the first magazines devoted exclusively to the new pastime. Within five years of the hobby's birth there were three American bottle magazines circulating nationally and at least a dozen with wide readership in one or more states.

Bottle shows also evolved rapidly during this period. Initially they were little more than swap-meetings where local collectors gathered perhaps once every two or three months to exchange unwanted bottles. As organised events they were particularly important to the growth of the hobby in the United States because, unlike British collectors who usually dig in large groups on large sites where there is ample opportunity to meet, swap and talk, most Americans spend their digging time on very small dumps where only two or three people can dig at one time. In order to meet fellow enthusiasts to exchange finds and talk 'shop' it was necessary for American collectors to hold their get-togethers either in collectors' homes or in clubhouses large enough to accommodate all the members of a group.

As the hobby grew in popularity and the number of collectors attending swap-meetings began to increase enterprising local businessmen—particularly those connected with the sale of bottled drinks—began to appreciate the advertising opportunities which might be gained by sponsoring the bottle collecting hobby. With financial help from these businessmen club secretaries were able to stage bigger and better meetings. Exhibitions of bottles found by members became regular features at most events and they attracted large crowds prepared to pay entrance fees to see the displays.

At inter-State level rivalry between clubs to stage the most crowd-catching exhibitions intensified and it was in order to promote higher standards of display at these events that club organisers introduced the element of competition between small collectors. During the early stages of the hobby's growth most clubs had restricted their displays to bottles owned by their own club members; now such restrictions were dropped and competitions for the best displays were thrown open to all-comers. Although the prizes awarded to winners were of no great value, the prestige of winning an open competition was very great indeed and it was not long before those collectors with exceptionally attractive or valuable bottles were travelling state-to-state to compete at bottle shows throughout America.

Because there were so many newcomers to the hobby with only modest collections but with high hopes of winning show prizes, methods of organising and judging competitions to give both beginners and experienced collectors equal opportunities to win were introduced. The number of categories in which bottles could be entered in these competitions were increased to include both common and modern bottles, and judges were encouraged to award more points for showmanship and display. Thus even an absolute beginner at the hobby could compete and even win a prize if he or she displayed an entry with flair and imagination.

The categories adopted by the majority of clubs were: historical flasks; bitters; inks; patent medicines; sealed bottles; sodas; fruit jars and other household bottles; blue glass; modern bottles and reproductions.

The decisions by show organisers to broaden the categories of bottles which could be entered in competitions and to encourage showmanship in display had far-reaching effects

97

on the hobby in the United States. The high standards of exhibition achieved by competitors attracted even greater interest from the uninitiated and thus swelled the ranks of bottle collectors. At the same time newcomers were encouraged to excavate bottles from dumps which experienced collectors had previously regarded as too modern to hold bottles worth collecting. Even those unable to find an old dump on which to dig could now satisfy their desires to own bottles and enter competitions by concentrating their collecting activities on modern bottles such as cosmetics, whisky figurals and fruit preserving jars recovered from old cellars. In addition the majority of collectors were now obliged to specialise in one particular category of bottles; with so much fierce competition to own the best bottles in each group there were only a few fortunate enthusiasts able to compete in all categories.

By the mid-1960's bottle collecting had become so popular that in many States the larger nineteenth century dumps were completely exhausted. Bottles excavated from them had by this time become recognised antiques, as likely to be seen in the windows of American antique shops as on the display shelves of bottle collectors. (It was not until 1973 that Victorian bottles were sold by British antique dealers.) The values of many of these pre-1900 bottles now began to increase rapidly and it was not long before they were far too expensive for the pockets of most beginners. At this point several enterprising bottle factories in the United States began to make inexpensive reproductions of some of the most prized American bottles and to offer them for sale to collectors unable to find or afford genuine items. Response to these reproductions was so great a number of glassworks were soon turning out large quantities of these 'instant antiques' and the collecting of them became a recognised branch of the American bottle scene. In addition to copying the earliest American bottles these glassmakers also produced large numbers of figural bottles as special orders for clubs, whisky distillers, and cosmetic packagers.

Many of these were made in limited numbers and their moulds were destroyed on completion of the batch. As a result some of the reproductions became even more valuable than genuine nineteenth century bottles and today there are thousands of collectors in the United States who specialize in this branch of the hobby.

The very full calendar of social events in which any American collector can involve himself includes bottle shows, swap-meetings and sales on almost every weekend of the year; national exhibitions staged by large clubs, glass manufacturers, and museums; and dozens of conferences, conventions, annual dinners, and other friendly get-togethers. In order to keep himself informed about current prices, collecting trends, or the latest issues of reproduction bottles he has a choice of dozens of magazines, newsletters and pamphlets and he can select from over two hundred books on specialised aspects of the hobby should he need more detailed information on his particular interests. The only requirement lacking from his otherwise total enjoyment of the hobby is probably a good nineteenth century dump because it is unfortunately a fact that the country which has more bottlelovers than all other countries put together is desperately short of sites on which these enthusiasts can dig. Those vast dumps on the outskirts of major urban and industrial centres which so inhibit the spirit of adventure in British diggers were, in the United States, long ago totally excavated or covered by skyscrapers and freeways. Even the more accessible ghost town dumps of California have been picked so clean that broken bottles are difficult to find and the chances of turning up a good whisky or bitters specimen are very slim indeed. The few sites yet to be found all lie in wild country and they are unlikely to contain more than the refuse from a single abandoned farm or homestead. Weeks of foot slogging effort and backbreaking probe rod work must be put in in order to locate them.

Because old dumps are in such short supply those Americans who do dig for their prizes have become highly skilled at site excavation. Deep and methodical digging, careful backfilling and sifting of soil to recover small items missed while trenching are painstakingly carried out by the vast majority of diggers in the United States. Their approach to site digging is that of the archaeologist determined to glean every scrap of historical material it might hold. Nothing is missed because so much time and effort has gone into finding the site it would be unthinkable to leave even the commonest of bottles behind.

Colonial bottles and Historical flasks. Prior to the Declaration of Independence (1776) the American Colonies were almost totally dependent on Europe for supplies of bottles and other containers. The majority were shipped from Britain, though France, Germany and other European countries also supplied American needs at this time. Many superb examples of seventeenth and eighteenth century European bottle making craftmanship have been excavated from colonial dumps in the New England states and recovered by divers from wreck sites on the Atlantic coast. A few rare examples, probably from the very earliest American glassworks in Jamestown, Virginia (early seventeenth century), and Salem, Massachusetts (mid seventeenth century) have also been found, but it was not until the eighteenth century that America had its first important glassworks. This was established in 1739 at Salem County, New Jersey, by Caspar Wistar and was in operation until 1779 producing a variety of household bottles for gin, snuff, mustard and other products. The bottles made by Wistar were similar in shape and colour to contemporary European products.

Bottles found

Another early American bottlemaker was Henry William Stiegel who operated his glassworks at Manheim, Pennsylvania from 1763 to 1774 and produced, in addition to common household bottles, a range of beautiful flint glass 'pocket bottles' in amethyst and sapphire blue glass and some fine engraved and enamelled decanters.

Other famous early American glasshouses include the Pitkin factory built near Hartford, Connecticut, in 1783, which produced Pitkin flasks in shades of amber and green until the 1830's; and the Dyottville Glassworks in Pennsylvania owned by 'Doctor' Thomas W. Dyott, one of America's first quack medicine vendors, from the 1820's until 1838. In addition to a wide range of household bottles the glassworks also produced copies of several English patent medicine bottles (e.g. Daffy's Elixir and Turlington's Balsam of Life) when supplies of these bottles (and presumably their contents) were cut off during the War of 1812. Genuine Dyottville bottles and those manufactured by Stiegel, Wistar and the Pitkin factory are so highly prized in the United States it is most unlikely any would be offered for sale or trade to overseas collectors.

Less valuable, though almost as highly prized, are the historical and pictorial whisky flasks produced in America during the period 1800–80. These mould-blown and richly embossed half-pint, one-pint and quart flasks were made by dozens of American glassworks and sold to whisky distillers throughout the land who used them in sales promotion campaigns which relied heavily on the intense spirit of patriotism that gripped the United States during the early nineteenth century. Embossing on the earliest examples included busts of presidents and presidential candidates, the American flag, the American eagle, and other patriotic decorations which induced people to buy the bottles regardless of the quality of the whisky they contained. Their popularity was an important factor in the growth of bottle-making in the United States; had it not been for the large and regular orders received by American glassworks for these flasks the industry might not have survived against foreign competition. Fortunately the bottles were required in vast quantities (millions were produced during their long period of popularity) and in over one thousand different designs which kept American mould-makers and glass-blowers profitably employed for more than seventy years.

There is a striking similarity in the type of subjects embossed on American whisky flasks during this period and those used to decorate British clay tobacco pipes during the years 1880–1900. At first only the portraits of important public figures were used; later masonic emblems and flags enjoyed a period of popularity, as did the faces of nationally-known figures from the worlds of theatre and music hall. The production of flasks (and pipes) to mark special events such as the opening of a railroad or the invention of a new type of bicycle also enjoyed a brief period of popularity but dwindling markets finally obliged manufacturers to restrict designs to abstract patterns, makers' names, and other markings which did not date rapidly.

Because of their enormous popularity as collectors' items historical flasks have been reproduced in substantial numbers during recent years. Many reproductions are made in strikingly colourful glass even though the majority of originals were made in aqua and shades of green. A few originals were also made with amber glass and an even smaller number in blue.

NOTES ON RARITY

There are few collectors in the United States who exclude historical flasks from their collections even though they probably specialize in other bottles. This popularity is reflected in prices which are high even for the flasks bearing the commonest embossings such as the American flag or eagle. British and Australian collectors might persuade Americans to part with some of the commoner examples in exchange for rare bitters and sealed bottles.

It is worth noting that although these flasks were not manufactured outside the United States (apart from a few reproductions made in Europe) they are occasionally found in British and Australian dumps. I have seen several examples bearing abstract design in Australian collections and one fine specimen bearing the portrait of George Washington which was dug from a dump in Liverpool, England. Others must await discovery.

Historical flasks; commoner varieties. Rating: Rare. Price guide : 100.
   rare varieties. Rating : Extremely difficult to obtain. Price guide: 150+.
Note: Several excellent books listing and pricing all known bottles in this group have been published in the United States. They should be referred to by any digger who unearths a specimen.

Bitters. The number of different bitters bottles found by diggers in the United States approaches one thousand five hundred. Some varieties such as Dr. J. Hostetter's Celebrated Stomach Bitters, have been found in tens of thousands; others, such as Dinger's Napoleon Cocktail Bitters, are so rare less than a dozen specimens are owned by collectors. Whether common or rare, bitters form a most important category within American bottle collecting and there are thousands of enthusiasts who devote their entire collections to this particular group of glass antiques.

The habit of drinking bitters as an alternative to whisky and gin was first popularised in the United States in 1785 when a respected doctor named Benjamin Rush published a manuscript titled *An Inquiry into the effects of Ardent Spirits on the Human Mind and Body.* Dr. Rush condemned drink and emphasised that many workmen habitually squandered family funds on alcohol. His outburst against the demon drink was given wide publicity in the American press and as a result many anti-liquor groups were formed. There were of course many people who scoffed at Dr. Rush and the anti-booze lobby and continued to consume vast quantities of whisky and gin; but substantial numbers turned to bitters which often contained more alcohol than whisky and gin in spite of the fact that it was sold as a medicine.

The consumption of bitters rose steadily in the United States until 1862. In that year a revenue tax was introduced to help pay for the Civil War. Whisky and gin were heavily taxed, but bitters, being classed as a medicine, was exempted from taxation. Inevitably this resulted in an enormous increase in bitters sales and in the number of quacks and shysters who bottled and marketed the 'medicine'.

For the next forty-five years, until the introduction in 1907 of the Pure Food and Drugs Act, a remarkably successful fraud was perpetrated against the American people by a small army of confidence tricksters who sold millions of gallons of rot-gut spirit under the name of bitters. To aid their sales campaigns they published large newspaper advertisements claiming miraculous cures of all manner of complaints from baldness to blindness; they introduced the world to the foot-in-the-door salesman; they even succeeded by a clever combination of psychology and hocus-pocus to convince large numbers of their customers that the 'medicines' really did what they claimed. Some eventually went to jail; others grew exceedingly rich and retired gracefully as multi-millionaires when the bitters boom ended early in the twentieth century. Their legacy to present-day bottle collectors is a rich assortment of delightful bottles, many of them embossed with outrageous and amusing trade names, all of them worthy of space on the shelves of any collector of nineteenth century bottles.

The characteristic bitters bottle shape is square with sloping shoulders and bevelled corners, usually made in either amber or aqua glass. Approximately fifty specimens are known in which this basic shape was developed to produce a log-cabin effect. Round bottles were also used by a substantial number of bitters firms and one or two used triangular, six-sided, eight-sided and twelve-sided bottles. Some of the most highly prized specimens are included in the small group which used figural bottles other than log-cabins. They are: Angostura Bark Bitters (globe); Barto's Great Gun Bitters (cannon); Berkshire Bitters (pig); Brown's Celebrated Indian Herb Bitters (Indian queen); Dingen's Napoleon Cocktail Bitters (drum); Doctor

Fisch's Bitters (fish); The Fish Bitters (fish); Herkules Bitters (ball); Horse Shoe Bitters (horse shoe); McKeever's Army Bitters (drum); National Bitters (ear of corn); General Scott's Artillery Bitters (cannon); Seaworth Bitters (lighthouse); Simon's Centennial Bitters (bust of soldier); Sol Frank's Panacea Bitters (lighthouse); Suffolk Bitters (pig).

Fig. 48 (*Top left*) Historical flask with American eagle embossed

Fig. 49 (*Top right*) Historical flask with abstract pattern. Amber coloured glass

NOTES ON RARITY

I recall seeing several years ago an advertisement in an American bottle magazine which read: 'Bitters bottles for sale; one to one hundred dollars'. Today's prices are much higher, but their range remains as wide. Fortunately there are many very attractive bottles at the lower end of the price scale and overseas collectors should have little difficulty in obtaining specimens of the most popular brands. Diggers who find examples of American bitters bottles in foreign dumps should pay particular attention to glass colour when

Fig. 50 European 'onio
bottle recovered from
wreck off America's ea
coast

Fig. 51 European seale
bottle from a wreck off tl
Florida coast

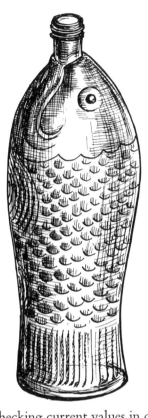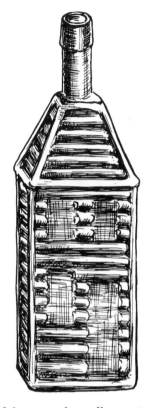

Fig. 52 (*Left*) Fish figural bitters bottle from a dump in California

Fig. 53 (*Right*) Log cabin bitters bottle from Maine

checking current values in one of the several excellent price guides to bitters bottles published in the United States. Bottles made for the export market or by foreign glassworks often differ in colour from specimens found in American dumps and these specimens are of considerable interest to collectors in the United States. A bottle rated in an American price guide as very common in amber glass might be extremely rare when the glass is black or bright green.

Bitters; common varieties. Price guide: 10+.
    scarce varieties. Price guide: 40+.
    rare varieties. Price guide: 70+.
Note: Comprehensive bitters price guides are available in the United States.

Inks. Small glass inks were among the first bottles to be made by American glassworks in the eighteenth century. They were purchased in one or two dozen lots by chemists and apothecaries who made their own ink, filled and labelled the bottles by hand, and sold the product to local customers. Early in the nineteenth century the manufacture of ink was organized on a fairly large scale in the United States and the factories producing it were able to supply most of the country's needs. For this reason very few British ink bottles are found in America by present-day dump diggers.

Evidence brought to light by digging tools reveals that America's nineteenth century ink manufacturers were much more aware of the sales potential of attractive containers than were their contemporaries in Britain. They used a wide variety of bottles including cones, barrels, umbrellas, igloos, teakettles, and figurals in addition to copying such British designs as eight-siders, boats, and squares. The majority of America's nineteenth century inks were also embossed either with the names of ink manufacturers or the glassworks that made the bottles.

Cones, or 'conical inks' as they were called in manufacturers' catalogues, had a long run of popularity in the United States. They were made from the early 1800's up to the introduction of machine-made bottles at the beginning of the twentieth century. The shape was very practical; it made the bottle difficult to overturn. Carter's Ink Company, one of the largest American ink manufacturers, used cone inks in vast quantities; specimens found by diggers include aquas, blues, and dark greens.

Umbrella inks—referred to as 'conical panelled inks' in manufacturers' catalogues—enjoyed a similar period of popularity and were also made in aqua, blues, and dark green glass. The majority are eight-siders, though ten, twelve, and sixteen-siders have also been found.

Igloo inks—termed 'domed inks with offset necks' in manufacturers' catalogues—were introduced in America in the 1860's and used by many ink makers for approximately twenty years. Aqua specimens are commonly found; amber, blue, and green varieties are rare. Teakettle inks, which resemble igloos but have sloping necks, are similarly dated.

The barrel-shaped and cylindrical glass ink bottles found by American diggers include hundreds of specimens with capacities ranging from a quarter pint to one gallon. Collectors in the United States call these bottles 'master inks'; they are the American equivalent of British bulk inks which, as every British digger knows, are all stoneware specimens. No satisfactory explanation why Americans favoured glass for these large and often fragile bottles has been put forward; perhaps American potteries were less competitive in their prices than were Britain's nineteenth century stoneware ink makers. Whatever the reason for the choice of glass, these master inks are identical in shape to British pottery specimens. The majority are aqua; blues are rare.

The range of figural inks available to collectors in the United States is considerably wider than in Britain and Australia. The human figures used by the Carter Ink Company are the commonest types, but glass specimens in the shape of boots, locomotives, and dogs are also found. As in Britain, the most prized figurals are those of cabin and house shapes. They first appeared in the United States in the 1840's and various designs from humble log cabins to stately mansions were issued by American glassworks up to the beginning of the twentieth century.

The vast majority of inks found in American dumps have neatly finished lips, usually of the laid-on-ring type. The few sheared lip specimens found are almost all of British make.

NOTES ON RARITY

British and Australian collectors should be pleasantly surprised by the range of relatively inexpensive inks available in America. Many of the commoner cones, umbrellas and

Fig. 54 American figural ink

Fig. 55 American figural ink

Fig. 56 Mr. & Mrs. Carter figural ink bottles

igloos are, by British and Australian standards, very low priced, though extremely high prices are asked and paid for many pontil-marked or unusually embossed specimens in these groups. There are thousands of collectors who specialize in inks and several excellent price catalogues covering almost every ink bottle found in the United States have been published. Diggers should refer to these before selling or offering for exchange any unusual ink bottles they find. Most American collectors are interested in obtaining sheared lip inks from Britain and Australia, especially bell-shaped inks and any specimens in blue or dark green glass.

Fig. 57   Master ink in cobalt blue glass. 20-oz capacity

Cone; aqua or clear. Rating: Fairly common. Price guide: 10.
   blue or deep green. Rating: Uncommon. Price guide: 15.
Umbrella; aqua or clear; eight-sided. Rating: Fairly common. Price guide: 10.
   blue or deep green; eight-sided. Rating: Uncommon. Price guide: 15.
   with ten or more sides. Rating: Uncommon. Price guide: 20+.
Igloo; aqua. Rating: Fairly common. Price guide: 20.
   amber, blue, deep green. Rating: Rare. Price guide: 50+
Teakettle: as above.
Master ink; quarter pint to one gallon capacity. Rating: Fairly common. Price guide: 10+.
Stoneware; cone. Rating: Rare. Price guide: 25.
   round. Rating: Fairly common. Price guide: 10.
Carter's Figural; man or woman. Rating: Fairly common. Price guide: 25.
Boot, locomotive, dog. Rating: Uncommon. Price guide: 50+.
Log cabin. Rating: Rare. Price guide: 150+.
Cottage or house. Rating: Extremely rare. Price guide: 200+.

Patent medicines. Colonial America was almost totally dependent on Britain for supplies of patent medicines. Large shipments of such well-known brands as Staughton's Elixir, Daffy's Elixir and Robert Turlington's Balsam of Life were despatched across the Atlantic to ease the aches and pains of the first settlers. These supplies were interrupted during the Revolutionary War and American chemists and apothecaries were obliged to concoct imitations and to invent and bottle their own cures in order to stay in business. Although supplies of many of the two hundred or so British medicines then on sale were resumed after the war, much of the market had by that time been lost to American products which were generally cheaper. Almost one hundred of these American brands were on sale by the beginning of the nineteenth century.

The earliest American medicines were packaged in unembossed bottles bearing paper labels, but as early as 1810 Thomas W. Dyott was advertising his 'Doctor Robertson's Patent Medicines' in American-made bottles embossed with this trade name. As already mentioned, Dyott also made at his Dyottville Glassworks embossed copies of Turlington's and Daffy's bottles, as did several other early nineteenth century American bottlemakers. These copies so closely resemble British originals it is often impossible for present-day collectors to tell which were American-made and which were British exports.

By the 1870's there were at least forty thousand patent medicines on sale in the United States and the industry had a turnover of eighty million dollars per year. These staggering figures can be largely accounted for by a combination of high-pressure salesmanship and confidence trickery; but there were other important factors which helped make nineteenth century Americans the world's greatest consumers of quack medicines. Between 1800 and 1860 the number of newspapers published in the United States rose from two hundred to four thousand. In the 1840's postal rates for printed material were greatly reduced by the American

Government and this resulted in massive increases in newspaper circulation figures. Quack medicine manufacturers took advantage of this situation by placing large advertisements in every newspaper in the land and by mailing vast quantities of misleading sales literature to prospective customers. The sale of bitters was only a small part of the patent medicine market; all other medicines also benefited from tax exemption in 1862 in spite of the fact that, like bitters, they contained large amounts of alcohol. A substantial number also contained opiates and many farmers, backwoodsmen and miners became addicted to them while trying to cure ingrowing toenails, consumption, and gout.

Medicine-shows, which achieved their greatest popularity in the late 1880's, also boosted sales of many nostrums. They ranged in size from the lone 'Doctor' with his covered-waggon load of newly bottled elixir who toured the frontier settlements to circus-sized exhibitions capable of attracting large crowds even in the sophisticated cities of the east. One of the most famous was the Kickapoo Indian Show owned and operated by the Kickapoo Medicine Company of Newhaven, Connecticut. This organization recruited a large number of Indians and claimed in its advertising literature they were the Kickapoo Tribe whose secret herbal remedies were bottled by the company. The products were sold between acts in the show which included war dances, horse riding feats, and other crowd-catching excitements. The popularity of this show can be gauged by the fact that it often grossed four thousand dollars in sales during a single show and that it toured Europe and Australia.

Other quack medicine vendors whose fame—and bottles— spread beyond America's shores included William Radam and his Microbe Killer, Perry Davis who marketed a pain killer containing fifty-two per cent alcohol, H. H. Warner whose bottles were embossed with a safe because he had been a safe salesman before he turned to nostrums, and Lydia Pinkham whose remedies for female complaints were known the world over.

The death knell of the patent medicine vendor was sounded in 1905 when Samuel Hopkins Adams wrote a series of articles under the title, *The Great American Fraud* for *Collier's Magazine*. His revelations—backed by irrefutable medical evidence—that millions of his countrymen were poisoning themselves with alcohol and opium whenever they opened a patent medicine bottle shocked the American public and forced many quack doctors into bankruptcy. The Pure Food and Drugs Act of 1907 ensured that the few who continued in business drastically altered both the contents of their bottles and the methods used to sell the products.

NOTES ON RARITY

Of the ten thousand or so embossed patent medicines found by diggers in the United States only ten per cent are rated highly by American collectors. These include specimens which can be dated, either by pontil marks or by contemporary newspaper advertisements and trade catalogues, earlier than 1860, and those of unusual shape or colour. The remainder—all aqua or clear glass bottles—are so numerous they do not command high prices even though they are elaborately embossed with picturesque trade marks or amusing advertising slogans. For example, the following aqua and clear glass specimens were, in 1974, priced at less than $U.S.10:

Fig. 58 'Kickapoo' medic bottle

Mysterious Pain Ease. A Scotch Remedy (Clear; oval; flaired lip).
Dr. James' Cherry Tar Syrup (Aqua; rect.; applied lip).
Brother Benjamine's Tar Syrup (Aqua; rect,; applied lip).
Dr. F. M. Clark's Herbalo Blood Purifier (Aqua; cylind.; applied lip).
Hanford's Celery Cure for Rheumatism, Neuralgia, Sleeplessness, Heart Trouble and Nervous Disorders (Aqua; rect.; applied lip).

Thousands of similar bargains are available to British and Australian collectors of patent medicine bottles who should have little difficulty in finding American collectors prepared to trade these greatly undervalued bottles for common British inks and Australian case gins.

Warner's Safe Cure, Rochester, N.Y.; amber-brown, Rating: Fairly common. Price guide: 25.
Radam's Microbe Killer; amber. Rating: Fairly common. Price guide: 30.
Dr. Kilmer's Swamp Root Kidney Cure; aqua. Rating; Common. Price guide: 1.
Sarsaparillas. Rating: Eagerly collected by many Americans. Price guide: 40+.
Early American specimens (pre 1860). Rating: Rare. Price guide: 60+.
Late 19th Century specimens in aqua or clear glass. Rating: Common. Price guide: 1–5.

Fig. 59 Late nineteenth century aqua medicine bottle

Fig. 60 American Warner's 'Safe' Cure from Rochester, New York

Whiskies and gins. In spite of temperance movements and the bitters vogue nineteenth century Americans consumed large quantities of whisky and gin. The historical flasks already discussed were almost all made for whisky distillers and it was the regular demand for spirits bottles which kept many American glassworks in business during the first half of the century.

When public interest in historical flasks bearing nationalistic and political embossing began to wane in the 1860's a number of whisky vendors turned to figurals. Most famous of these were the amber log-cabin bottles used by the E. Booz Company of Philadelphia and the figural whiskies issued by the Bininger Grocery Company of New York between 1820 and 1880. The Bininger bottles included clocks, cannons, and other interesting shapes and they were made in amber, green and puce coloured glass.

A standard whisky bottle of cylindrical shape and with a

capacity of one fifth of a gallon came into general use in the United States in the late 1860's. Although the majority of these were made in aqua and clear glass they were often elaborately embossed and these specimens are eagerly collected today. Pumpkin seeds and coffin flasks of half and one-pint capacities were also widely used as whisky bottles between 1880 and 1900. Transfer-printed pottery jugs were popular but the quality of the transfers was much inferior to those found on Scotch and Irish whisky jugs of the same period which also turn up in small numbers in American dumps. Few of the American-made jugs carried pictorial designs, but they are, nevertheless, enthusiastically collected and early specimens fetch good prices.

The vast majority of American glass whisky bottles were made in aqua or clear glass; amber specimens are uncommon; black glass is rare. All of them used cork stoppers up to the beginning of the twentieth century.

Like Britain and Australia, the United States depended heavily on Holland for supplies of gin during the eighteenth and nineteenth centuries. Large numbers of Dutch case gin bottles and square Schnapps bottles are found by American diggers; but, as in Britain, specimens bearing shoulder seals are rare. There are, however, considerably more embossed gin and Schnapps bottles in American dumps than have yet been found in Britain and this has encouraged many collectors to specialize in this group.

Of the nineteenth century Dutch gin and Schnapps distillers whose embossed bottles are found in Australian dumps the following are also found—in fewer numbers— in the United States: A. C. Nolet; Blankenheim & Nolet; V. Hoytema; Lucas Bols; Jurgen & Peters; Van der Zee & Co.; Pollen & Zoon; Levert & Schadels; J. T. Gayen; Meyer's; Ellwinch & Zoon; Van Diepen & Co.; A. van Hoboken; A. Houtman; E. Kiderlen; J. H. Henkes; Udolpho Wolfe.

Rarer finds include the Willem Zoon's Cosmopoliet Gin bottle bearing the embossed figure of a man; a C. W.

Fig. 61 Pumpkin seed whisky flasks

Herwig bottle embossed with a corkscrew; and an amber figural in the shape of a coachman embossed, 'Van Dunk's Genever'. Large numbers of eighteenth and early nineteenth century free-blown case gins without shoulder seals but with crude pontil marks are also to be seen in American collections. Many have come from wreck sites.

NOTES ON RARITY

Scotch and Irish whisky bottles—especially black glass and transfer-printed stoneware specimens—are in great demand in the United States, as are all varieties of sealed case gins. British and Australian diggers able to supply these items will find a ready market. In return American collectors should be able to supply stoneware whisky jugs and large numbers of embossed aqua whisky bottles.

Whisky; Booz log-cabin figural. Rating: Extremely rare.
  Price guide: 200+.

Bininger specimens. Rating: Rare. Price guide: 150+.
Pumpkin seed; pictorial embossing. Rating: Uncommon. Price guide: 25+.
Coffin flasks; pictorial embossing. Rating: Uncommon. Price guide: 20+.
Scotch and Irish transfer-printed specimens. Rating: Rare. Price guide: 80.
American specimens. Rating: Fairly common. Price guide: 20.
Aqua; cylindrical. Rating: Very common. Price guide: 3.

Gin and Schnapps; early freeblown case. Rating: Rare. Price guide: 50+.
Shoulder sealed. Rating: Rare. Price guide: 50+.
Embossed. Rating: Uncommon. Price guide: 40+.
Pictorial embossing. Rating: Rare. Price guide: 50+.
Figural. Rating: Very rare. Price guide: 100.

Fig. 62   American b
glass whisky bottle

Mineral and soda waters. Americans use the term 'mineral waters' to describe naturally mineralized spring waters which were first bottled and sold in the American colonies in the mid-eighteenth century. The most famous of the spas from which these waters came was the Saratoga Spring in Saratoga County, New York. In the 1840's the company which owned it was bottling the waters in attractive olive-green and olive-amber embossed bottles with cork stoppers. Sales reached several millions of bottles per year by the 1850's and from then until the close of the century some three dozen different bottles were used by the company.

Another famous spa was Poland Spring near Portland, Maine. In 1876 the waters were bottled in an attractive green figural in the shape of a bearded Moses which proved immensely popular. Thirteen different models of the 'Moses bottle' were introduced between 1876 and 1930 when it was used—by the same company—as a gin bottle.

European spa waters were also exported to the United States in the nineteenth century to satisfy emigrant demand.

The most popular brand was Apollinaris Water which came from Germany in stoneware bottles. Waters from British and French spas were also shipped to the United States in glass bottles.

The popularity of natural mineral waters dwindled after the Civil War when increasing numbers of Americans began to acquire the habit of drinking artificially carbonated and flavoured waters. The most popular of these drinks was flavoured soda water which, by 1870, was the most widely consumed non-alcoholic beverage on sale in the U.S.A. The bottles in which it was first sold are called 'blob-top sodas' by American collectors. They have the bulbous applied lips seen on Hamilton bottles in Britain and Australia, but their bodies are cylindrical and flat-bottomed. In 1875 the Lightning Stopper—a porcelain or rubber plug attached to the outside of the bottle by wire bales which controlled opening and closing—was invented by Charles de Quillfeldt. Although adopted by many soda water manufacturers it did not achieve long-term popularity because in 1879 an equally efficient but much less expensive stopper was invented. This—the Hutchinson Stopper—consisted of a rubber gasket which formed a gas-tight seal against the inside walls of the bottle's neck when it was pulled into the closed position by means of a looped piece of wire. The stopper was to prove the most popular closure for soda water bottles until the invention by William Painter in 1891 of the Crown Cork still widely used on soft drinks bottles today.

Although Charles Hutchinson, inventor of the Hutchinson Stopper, had a number of rivals in the late nineteenth century who either made close copies of his stopper or tried variations on British internal stoppers, only three types of bottles—blob-tops, Hutchinsons and Crown Corks—achieved long-term popularity. A small number of soda water manufacturers used British Codd's and Hamiltons, but present-day soda water bottle collectors in the United States have nothing like the range of unusual closures seen in British and Australian collections. They do have a wide range of embossments to chose from and a limited colour range of aqua, amber, and a few blue specimens.

NOTES ON RARITY

British and Australian collectors should have no difficulty in acquiring examples of American Hutchinson stoppers which are fairly common in aqua glass. The early bottles used for natural mineral waters are much more valuable.

Mineral water; Saratoga Spring; early specimen. Rating: Rare. Price guide: 80.
later issues. Rating: Uncommon. Price guide: 30.
Moses figural; early specimen. Rating: Rare. Price guide: 100.
later issues. Rating: Uncommon. Price guide: 50+.
European stoneware. Rating: Uncommon. Price guide: 20.
Soda water; blob-top; aqua. Rating: Fairly common. Price guide: 15.
other colours. Rating: Rare. Price guide: 50+.
Lightning stopper. Rating: Difficult to find. Price guide: 30+.
Hutchinson Stopper; aqua. Rating: Fairly common. Price guide: 15.
other colours. Rating: Rare. Price guide: 40+.
Crown Cork. Rating: Common. Price guide: 1.

Fig. 63 Hutchinson-stoppered bottle

Fruit jars and household bottles. The collecting of fruit preserving jars is a popular branch of the hobby in the United States, especially with newcomers who can acquire common specimens at very little cost. Not that all fruit jars are inexpensive; dedicated enthusiasts regularly pay hundreds of dollars for rare specimens with unusual closures or glass colour. The earliest finds in this category are eighteenth and early nineteenth century imports. Few are embossed but most bear rough pontil marks. Large cork stoppers were used on these jars; after the fruit had been placed in the jar the cork was forced into the neck with the aid of a wooden mallet before the jar was boiled in the sterilization process. Necks had to be strong to withstand this treatment and for this reason the applied lips on these early containers are exceptionally thick.

Because the preserving of fruit and vegetables by bottling was a popular and necessary activity in nineteenth century rural America many inventors attempted to improve on the simple cork closure. The first to achieve commercial success was John Landon Mason, a skilled tinsmith who, in 1858, developed a zinc screw lid for use on jars with threads moulded in their necks. These lids were cheap to manufacture and Mason's invention was quickly taken up by many glassmakers and their screw-threaded jars were given the name 'Mason jars'—even though Mason's company manufactured only the zinc lids.

A disadvantage of Mason's lid was that the zinc from which it was made came into direct contact with the food in the jar. To overcome this problem Salmon B. Rowley of the Hero Glass Company patented an all-glass lid in 1868. It consisted of a flat piece of glass which covered the mouth of the jar and was held in place by a metal screw cap. In the following year another inventor, Louis R. Boyd, improved on the Mason lid by providing it with a porcelain or milk-glass liner which prevented the contents of the jar coming in direct contact with the zinc and which also hid unsightly stains caused by seepage of the contents during storage. Boyd's invention was used by many fruit jar makers and helped keep Mason in business for many more years.

In 1875 Henry W. Putnam adapted a wire bale closure for use on fruit jars. Although it was less popular than Mason's, lid specimens are found in many present-day

collections. Other inventors—there were many who attempted to improve fruit jar closures during the late nineteenth century—had less commercial success and it is these little-used inventions which are found on the most highly-prized jars.

There was little variation in fruit jar sizes and shapes; all were cylindrical with wide mouths and of standard capacities and the vast majority were made in aqua glass. A dozen companies are known to have made amber jars and an even smaller number used black, emerald green, blue, and milk-glass. Earthenware fruit jars are equally difficult to find.

Household bottles and jars form another important category for a large number of beginners at the hobby in the United States. They include fluted peppersauces, cathedral-shaped pickle jars, stoneware blacking pots and a wide assortment of food containers. All of the glass specimens which were made in aqua or clear glass are inexpensive, though high prices are paid for the few examples found in emerald green, amber, or blue.

NOTES ON RARITY

Fruit jar; aqua; Mason type. Rating: Common. Price guide: 1–5.
other colours. Rating: Rare. Price guide: 40+.
other closures: Rating: Uncommon. Price guide: 30+.
Stoneware specimens. Rating: Rare. Price guide: 40.
Household; glass; aqua or clear. Rating: Common. Price guide: 1–5.
other colours. Rating: Uncommon. Price guide: 25+.
Stoneware. Rating: Common. Price guide: 1–5.

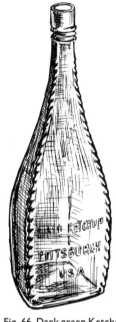

Fig. 66 Dark green Ketchup bottle from an early twentieth century American dump

Stoneware. In addition to a small number of stoneware pots and jars imported from Europe during the eighteenth and nineteenth centuries, American dump diggers find a large number of stoneware containers which fall roughly into two categories: Chinese pottery bottles and whisky jugs. The Chinese specimens are a legacy of the gold-rush and railroad-building days when great numbers of Chinese workers came to the United States and brought with them (or had sent from China) a wide variety of stoneware containers. Best known are the 'tiger whisky' bottles which held rice wine. They are bell-shaped and usually brown in colour. Some have hand-painted Chinese lettering. Miniature versions of these bottles are often mistakenly called 'opium pots' by many collectors. In fact they contained nothing more addictive than soy sauce.

American whisky jugs are generally larger than the transfer-printed Scottish and Irish specimens found by diggers in Britain and Australia. Many of them are transfer-printed but the transfers are rarely pictorial. Coloured transfers (blue on many of the earliest examples) are quite common. Shapes vary from squat, bulbous specimens which are generally accepted as having been made before 1880 to tall cylindrical jugs with sloping shoulders which were made up to 1920.

NOTES ON RARITY

Chinese bottles and American whisky jugs are common, but very high prices are paid for whisky jugs which can be dated pre-1880.

'*Tiger whisky*' *bottles*. Rating: Common. Price guide:1–5.
'*Opium pots*'. Rating: Fairly common. Price guide: 5–10.
Whisky jug; made after 1880. Fairly common. Price
    guide: 5–10.
    with pictorial transfer. Rating: Rare. Price guide: 40+.
    made before 1880. Rating: rare. Price guide: 50+.

Baby feeders. Americans call them 'nursers' and they are found with a wider range of embossing than those found in Britain, though shapes are generally similar. Cone-shaped specimens designed to stand on-end will be of most interest to British and Australian collectors as this type seems to be limited to the United States. Almost all American specimens were made in clear glass and most of those in collections have turned to beautiful shades of amethyst.

NOTES ON RARITY

Flattened oval. Rating: Fairly common. Price guide: 25.
Banana shape. Rating: Common. Price guide: 15.
Cone shape. Rating: Uncommon. Price guide: 30+.

Poison bottles. American diggers find a wider range of poison bottle shapes than are found in Britain and Australia. For

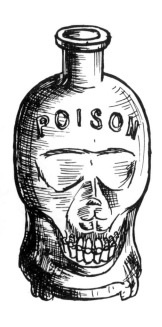

Fig. 67 (*Left*) Figural poison bottle

Fig. 68 (*Below*) Skull and cross-bones poison bottle

this reason there are many collectors who specialise in this category. The commonest poison container is the Tatum bottle which was patented in 1872. It is usually found in cobalt blue glass and it has raised dots on its surface which indicated that the bottle's contents were lethal. Triangular poison bottles are also fairly common and many are embossed with a skull and crossbones. Coffin-shaped poison bottles are not too difficult to find. Again the commonest colour is cobalt blue, but brown and green specimens are known. Rarer specimens include a number of figurals in the shape of skulls.

Fig. 69 Cobalt-blue poison bottle with raised pattern

Tatum bottle and others with raised patterns. Rating: Common. Price guide: 1–5.
Triangular. Rating: Fairly common. Price guide: 10.
  with skull and crossbones embossed. Fairly common. Price guide: 20.
Coffin shaped. Rating: Uncommon. Price guide: 30+.
Figurals. Rating: Rare. Price guide: 40+.

Fire grenades. Unlike British collectors who have to content themselves with only one variety of fire grenade, the American collector can chose from a wide range when buying these bottles. The Harden specimen known in Britain is probably the commonest American type found in blue glass. Other blue grenades include the Harkness Fire Destroyer, the Kalamazoo and the Y–Burn Winner. The Hayward Company of New York also produced a blue fire grenade. This company's output included specimens in amber, green and olive glass of cylindrical as well as ball-shape. The Harden Company of Chicago obviously had a world-wide market for their products which included a wide range of colours and shapes.

NOTES ON RARITY

Because these bottles were destroyed during use only

small numbers have survived. For this reason—and the fact that they are very attractive bottles—prices are high even for the well-known specimens.

Hardens: 40+.
Hayward's: 40+.
Others: 60+.

Note: Several books on fire grenades are available in the U.S.A. Most have up-to-date price guides listing all known varieties.

Reproduction bottles. The manufacture of reproduction bottles is a thriving industry in the United States where several large companies and numerous one-man glassworks turn out perfect copies of most of America's rarest historical flasks, bitters and patent medicine bottles. Most of these companies now mark their bottles with a batch number or a similar device to enable collectors to distinguish between these 'instant antiques' and genuine pre-1900 bottles. Such reproductions are an essential part of the American bottle collecting scene; without them many enthusiasts would be unable to enjoy the hobby because there are simply not enough pre-1900 bottles in the United States to provide all collectors with specimens for their display shelves. They should not be sold to or bought by collectors in Britain because of the danger that they might be taken for genuine specimens by British collectors who have no knowledge of the American reproductions market.

Modern bottles. The range of modern bottles collected in the United States is as least as wide as is the range of 'dug bottles' collected in Britain, Australia, *and* the United States put together. It includes such diverse groups as 'candy jars' of 1930's vintage which come in a wide variety of figural shapes; 'barber bottles' which when full contain hair preparations and which are still to be found in great profusion in American hairdressers' shops; decanters and bar bottles; the internationally-known Avon bottles; Jim Beam bottles which come in over two hundred and fifty different figural shapes; modern Luxardo bottles made in majolica-ware; and Garnier liqueur bottles which are made in France especially for the American market. In addition hundreds of bottle clubs and other organizations in the U.S.A. regularly commission glassmakers to produce commemorative figural bottles which are sold to members or given as prizes at bottle shows and similar meetings. These bottles are usually made in cobalt blue, ruby red, or amber glass. Like the reproduction bottles already mentioned these modern bottles help to stimulate and sustain interest in bottle collecting in a country which suffers from a grave shortage of pre-1900 dumps. Perhaps one day British collectors will also take an interest in these bottles, but at the present time they do not circulate outside of the United States.

Restored and repaired bottles. The American bottle collecting fraternity can be divided into two distinct groups: those who are happy to display on their shelves bottles which have been repaired, and those who refuse to own any bottle which has been tampered with in any way. The second group is larger, but because all pre-1900 bottles are scarce in the U.S.A. the first group grows daily as more and more collectors accept that they will never be able to obtain perfect specimens of certain rare bottles. It is these collectors who provide the market for bottles which have been re-paired with polyester resins and coated with oils and other substances to hide glass sickness. They can obtain all the specimens they require from American diggers.

Glass sickness, iridescence, and opalescence. Approximately fifty per cent of recovered bottles taken from American dumps suffer from sickness. The worst cases are to be found on bottles recovered from desert regions (e.g. Arizona) which are heavily encrusted with a whitish powdery deposit. 'Frosted' sickness is also commonly found on the many bottles recovered by divers in the U.S.A. who also find some of America's most beautiful iridescent and opalescent specimens in river mud.

Pontil marks. American collectors use the term 'open pontil' to describe the mark left by a solid iron bar pontil. The term 'ring pontil' is used to describe the ring-shape mark left by a blowpipe pontil. The terms 'improved pontil' and 'graphite pontil' are used to describe the white or reddish deposits found on some bottles which were held on a pontil rod during manufacture. In America such bottles can be accurately dated to 1845–70 if the deposit is reddish in colour, and to 1870–80 if a whitish deposit is seen.

Sun-coloured glass. Amethyst shading on bottles is common in America but the depth of purpling is rarely equal to Australian colouring except in the desert regions.

Books, clubs, magazines:

Books:

American Glass, G. McKearin, Crown Publishers Inc., New York, 1968.
The Official Bottle Price List, T. Kovel, Crown Publishers Inc., New York, 1972.
Bitters Bottles, R. Watson, Nelson & Sons, New York, 1968.
Fruit Jars, J. Toulouse, Nelson & Sons, New York, 1969.
Avon Price Guide, M. Holmberg, Western World Publishers, 1969.
Ink Bottles and Ink Wells, E. Covill, Sullwold Publishing, Mass., 1971.
Poisons, A Collectors' Guide, W. Stier, Antique and Hobby Publishing Co., Calif., 1973.
Ghost Town Bottle Price Guide, W. Bressie, Caxton Printers Ltd., Idaho, 1973.

Magazines:

Old Bottle Magazine, Bend, Oregon, 97701.
Bottles & Relics, Conroe, Texas.
Bottle News, Kermit, Texas, 79745.

Clubs:

There are several hundred clubs in the U.S.A. Check the above magazines for up-to-date addresses.

Dealers:

There are thousands of dealers. All of them advertise in the above magazines.

The Canadian Scene

Bottle diggers in Canada find much the same bottles as those found by diggers in the United States but there are rather more European bottles—especially British and French specimens—to be had. Prices for most bottles are similar to those in the United States though sun-coloured bottles are more expensive.

Books:

Only one book on bottle collecting has so far been published in Canada: *Western Canadian Bottle Collecting*, G. Watson, Evergreen Press, 1972.

During the past few years newspapers in almost every country in the world have published articles—from three-line fillers to full page illustrated features—on the bottle collecting hobby. Most have told their readers in amusing—and occasionally derogatory—terms of the 'eccentrics' in the United States, Britain, and Australia who spend their weekends digging into nineteenth century rubbish dumps to recover junk thrown away by their great-grandparents which is then carefully cleaned, restored and displayed with pride in the diggers' homes.

Most readers who have cast their eyes over these reports have, no doubt, shaken their heads in disbelief and turned to the political or sports pages; but a tiny minority have read with interest and, after equipping themselves with suitable digging tools, gone off in search of an old dump on which to try their luck. As a result there are, scattered throughout the newspaper-reading world, small groups of enthusiasts who find and preserve nineteenth century bottles and who derive much enjoyment from the hobby in spite of their isolation from the remainder of the bottle collecting fraternity.

The largest of these groups are the South Africans who have been bottle lovers for some time and who are likely to join the 'major league' of bottle collecting countries within a few years and to publish their own newsletter or magazine. At the present time activity is centred around the city of Port Elizabeth where a large nineteenth century dump is located on the outskirts of the city. It holds a wide assortment of British bottles—internally-stoppered mineral waters, blue poisons, black glass beers, inks and the like—and a rich variety of Dutch case gins bearing beautiful shoulder seals. Several of the diggers have managed to obtain copies of the British magazine *Bottles & Relics News* and have, through its columns, made contact with collectors in England. Recently one of their numbers wrote an article for the magazine which told of the pleasures and excitements of South African dump digging and indicated the group's intention to produce a newsletter and to broaden their contact with overseas collectors.

Another small but active group who find both British and Dutch bottles are based in Singapore. They are military personnel serving at air force and naval bases and some of them were already bitten by the bottle collecting bug before they left Britain for overseas duties. An adventurous group, they include in their activities scuba-diving in South-East Asian rivers and digs on abandoned native villages in jungle clearings. Their rewards for these efforts have been many rare and valuable finds including stoneware Bellarmines and eighteenth and early nineteenth century freeblown glass specimens of both Dutch and British origins.

In Europe there are isolated diggers at work in France, Germany, Holland, Italy and the Scandinavian countries. American forces personnel have helped to encourage local interest in Germany by digging old dumps around cities and towns near American bases. Although most of their finds have been proudly carried home to the United States, the bottles have been seen and appreciated by local citizens who have now joined the Americans on several sites.

Recently a friend of mine who owns a fine collection of British mineral water bottles showed his display to an Italian acquaintance who has lived in Britain for two or three years. After examining the collection with interest the Italian told my friend that such bottles could be picked up 'by the hundreds' along the banks of a river in Northern Italy. A quick change in the family's holiday plans was immediately made by the Briton and a few months later his wife and children were sunbathing on an Italian beach while he went off in search of this productive riverside dump. He found it—but the best bottles had already been recovered by a group of locals who had recently been converted to the hobby. Fortunately my friend had taken several British bottles with him on his holiday and after some tough trading he managed to acquire a Barnsley-made Codd richly embossed with an Italian trade mark. He also acquired several new bottle collecting friends with whom he somehow manages to exchange letters and finds, in spite of his knowing only half-a-dozen words of Italian.

Brief encounters—and a few which have resulted in lasting friendships and a good deal of bottle trading—have been made by other British bottle collectors on holiday in Europe. It is known that Danish diggers are finding superb transfer-printed pot lids, that small groups in France are recovering large numbers of ornate clay tobacco pipes, and that farm workers in Holland have recently been 'harvesting' a valuable crop of sealed case gins by ploughing a little deeper before planting sugarbeet and potatoes. Most of the finds have been sold to antique shops in Amsterdam and other cities, but a few of the farmers are now beginning to take great interest and are forming impressive collections.

In South America, where for many years American tourists have provided a market for antiques, interest in nineteenth century bottles has been encouraged by requests for such items made by visitors from San Francisco, New York and other U.S. cities. Many dumps in Mexico have been extensively dug—some by American bottle collectors who have travelled thousands of miles to reach the sites—and finds have included early Spanish, British and American glass and stoneware bottles. Further south, in Argentina, Brazil and Peru dumps containing early nineteenth century bottles from Spain, Portugal and other European countries have recently been located. There are, at the present time, very few local collectors and it is only because of a ready market for the bottles in the United States that hundreds of people are eagerly digging for them.

There can be no doubt that the future of bottle collecting as an international hobby lies in the dumps of those countries where there are at present few enthusiasts. The United States—birthplace and centre of the hobby—is rapidly exhausting its nineteenth century dumps; Australia, with its fast increasing population and very limited number of fair-sized dumps, has a similar problem; Britain, where most of the diggers are concentrated in the heavily-populated areas, could run out of readily accessible dumps within five to ten years. It is therefore of the utmost importance that enthusiasts in the United States, Australia and Britain encourage the growth of bottle collecting in neighbouring countries and that a much greater volume of international trading and exchanging is carried on, especially between Europe with its vast and as yet almost totally unexplored dump resources and the United States where more than seventy five per cent of the world's bottle collectors now live. I hope readers of this book will play their part in this important task.

Note:

> *Readers who live in countries where the hobby is still in an embryonic stage will, no doubt, eventually form clubs and publish books and magazines when bottle collecting attracts sufficient numbers of enthusiasts. If details of these organisations and publications are forwarded to the author he will endeavour to include them in future reprints of this book. Letters should be addressed to Edward Fletcher, 104 Harwal Road, Redcar, Cleveland, England.*

It is fortunate that the three countries in which bottle collecting has achieved its greatest popularity—the United States, Britain, and Australia—have, in addition to a common language, extremely efficient postal systems. Collectors and dealers in these countries who despatch bottles by overseas mail can be reasonably certain the bottles will reach their destinations safely—subject to one most important provision: packaging *must* be adequate for the journey.

Like most other collectors I learned the secrets of successful export bottle packaging the hard way and I have several broken specimens to certify my time-served apprenticeship. Readers who wish to gain less costly experience are advised to abide by the following tried and proven rules when sending bottles on overseas journeys:

1. Use shredded newspaper to encapsule each bottle. Tear up several newspapers and soak them in warm water for a few minutes before wrapping the pieces around the bottle until you have built up a 'cocoon' of wet paper at least half an inch thick.

Note. Do not be tempted to use straw or sawdust when packaging bottles for export. Both of these materials are disallowed by customs regulations in Britain, the United States, Australia, and many other countries.

2. Use a cardboard carton of the double-walled type obtainable free of charge at wine and spirits merchants' stores. These boxes usually have cardboard partitions within them and they are designed to carry one dozen full bottles of wine or spirits. When packaging *empty* bottles of approximately one-pint capacity which are to be despatched overseas only *two* 'cocooned' bottles should be placed in the box, using the two central compartments. The remaining ten compartments must be stuffed to capacity with dry, screwed-up newspapers, as should any space left in the two central compartments. A folded newspaper should also be placed over the top of the compartments before the outer flaps are secured with adhesive tape.

Note. When packaging smaller bottles (e.g. inks) you can

place two 'cocoons' in each of the central compartments. They should be separated by a tightly rolled ball of dry newspaper.

3. With the outer flaps secure put your package to the following test. Stand two yards from an upholstered chair and throw the box at the seat of the chair. If the springing in the chair is sound the box will hit the seat and bounce to the floor. It will receive rough treatment like this several times during its journey and it must survive without bursting open or splitting at the seams. If the box survives this test, and if you can carry out the test confident that you will not break the contents, then you have packaged your bottles securely.

4. The box can now be wrapped neatly in a sheet of strong brown paper. Use clear adhesive tape to complete the wrapping.

5. Address the package clearly and boldly using a black felt-tipped pen. Postal or Zip Codes are most important and should never be overlooked when addressing packages to the U.S.A. or Australia. Write the address on two sides of the box and add your own name and address (as sender) at both ends.

6. At the post office you will be given a Customs Declaration form which must be completed and secured to the package. Describe the contents of your package accurately.

7. I strongly advise all readers to send bottles overseas by airmail postage. It is several times more expensive than surface postage but there is no doubt that airmail packages receive considerably less rough treatment than do parcels sent by surface mail. A further advantage is that the package is delivered within days. It will take several weeks if you send it by surface mail. If you opt for the airmail service ask the post office clerk for half a dozen airmail stickers and place one on each end and side of the box.

8. When you pay the postage you will receive a certificate of postage. At the earliest opportunity you should photocopy this piece of paper and send the copy in an airmail

letter to the addressee. This will prove postage and also alert the addressee to expect delivery. Keep the original certificate in a safe place until the addressee confirms receipt of the package. You will require the certificate if you have to make a lost package claim.

A NOTE TO READERS SELLING BOTTLES TO OVERSEAS CUSTOMERS

It is common practice in bottle collecting circles to ask customers for payment in advance. Your customer should send a cheque to you made out in the currency of *your* country. If he does this you will be able to clear the cheque immediately. If it is made out in a foreign currency you will have to wait at least two weeks before the cheque is cleared.

When offering bottles for sale to prospective overseas buyers—especially when asking for payment in advance— it is of the utmost importance that you describe the bottles accurately. If possible you should send a clear photograph of each bottle. Be completely honest when describing a bottle's condition and never under any circumstances sell bottles which are sick, cracked, or chipped—however slight the imperfections. It may take several months and several dozen successful transactions to establish your reputation as a reliable dealer. You will destroy that reputation very quickly if any of the specimens you sell fall short of the descriptions you circulate to prospective customers.

'Acme' Codd bottles 23
Adams (Samuel H.) 114
Apollinaris Co 71
Australian Bottle Collectors Review 62, 94
Australian wines 78
AVH seals 40
Avon bottles 128

barber bottles 128
Barnett and Foster 24
barrel inks 30, 108
Barrett and Elers 24
bears' grease 55
bell inks 30
Bellarmine jugs 68
Bininger Grocery Company 115
boat inks 30
Booz Company 115
Bottles and Relics News 16
bottle shows 96
Bourne & Co 30
Breffit 24
British Bottle Collectors Club 16
'Bulb' Codd bottles 22

canals 14
candy jars 128
Cannington-Shaw 24
Cantrell & Cochrane 21
chemist's shop bottles 44
Codd-Hamilton hybrids 27
Codd (Hiram) 21
Codd's 'Original' 21, 24
coloured Codd bottles 24
coloured lip Codd bottles 23
cone inks 30, 108
Cosmopoliet Gin 80

cottage inks 30

Daffy's Elixir 112
Dagenham, Essex 14
Davis, Perry 113
Doulton & Watts 30
Dr. Dyott 46, 101, 112
Dr. Rush 103
Dr. Soule's Hop Bitters 34, 77
Drioli seals 36
Dutch East India Company 68

'Empress' Codd bottles 22
Essex marshes 13
Europe 133

figural inks 109

German bitters 34
ghost towns 95
Gledhill patent 72
Green (Stephen) & Co. 30

halfpenny syrups bottles 44
Hamilton bottles 21
Holland 19
Hutchinson stoppers 119

igloo inks 30, 108
Ireland 15

Jamestown, Virginia 100

Kent marshes 13
Kickapoo Medicine Company 113
Kilner Bros 24

lager beer   83
Lamont   24
'Lightning' stoppers   73
Lovatt & Co   30
Luxardo seals   36

Magazzin seals   36
Mason (John L.)   121
Maugham's patent   72

nipple pontil   59

Pinkham (Lydia)   113
Pitkin flasks   101
Poland Spring   118
Port Dundas pottery   30
Putnam (Henry W.)   121

Radam, William   113
'Reliance' Codd bottles   23
ring seal beers   81
Ross & Co   22, 71
Rylands, Ben   22
Rylands, Dan   22

Salem, Mass.   100
Saratoga Spring   118
Schiedam, Holland   40

Schweppe & Co   71
Scotland   15
sheared lip inks   29
Singapore   133
South Africa   132
South America   134
Stiegel (Henry W.)   100
Stiff & Co   30
Sutcliffe   24
Sykes-Magvay   24

teakettle inks   30
Thorne's whisky   41
three-sided inks   30
Turlington bottles   112

umbrella inks   30, 108

Valet   24
'Valve' Codd bottles   23

Wales   33
Warner (H. H.)   113
Wistar (Caspar)   100

Zara seals   36